Mathematics Describing the Real World: Precalculus and Trigonometry

Bruce H. Edwards, Ph.D

THE
GREAT
COURSES®

PUBLISHED BY:

THE GREAT COURSES
Corporate Headquarters
4840 Westfields Boulevard, Suite 500
Chantilly, Virginia 20151-2299
Phone: 1-800-842-2412
Fax: 703-378-3819
www.thegreatcourses.com

Bruce H. Edwards, Ph.D.
Professor of Mathematics
University of Florida

Professor Bruce H. Edwards has been a Professor of Mathematics at the University of Florida since 1976. He received his B.S. in Mathematics from Stanford University in 1968 and his Ph.D. in Mathematics from Dartmouth College in 1976. From 1968 to 1972, he was a Peace Corps volunteer in Colombia, where he taught mathematics (in Spanish) at La Universidad Pedagógica y Tecnológica de Colombia.

Professor Edwards's early research interests were in the broad area of pure mathematics called algebra. His dissertation in quadratic forms was titled "Induction Techniques and Periodicity in Clifford Algebras." Beginning in 1978, he became interested in applied mathematics while working summers for NASA at the Langley Research Center in Virginia. This led to his research in the area of numerical analysis and the solution of differential equations. During his sabbatical year 1984–1985, he worked on 2-point boundary value problems with Professor Leo Xanthis at the Polytechnic of Central London. Professor Edwards's current research is focused on the algorithm called CORDIC that is used in computers and graphing calculators for calculating function values.

Professor Edwards has coauthored a wide range of mathematics textbooks with Professor Ron Larson of Penn State Erie, The Behrend College. They have published leading texts in the areas of calculus, applied calculus, linear algebra, finite mathematics, algebra, trigonometry, and precalculus. This course is based on the bestselling textbook *Precalculus, A Graphing Approach* (5th edition, Houghton Mifflin, 2008).

Over the years, Professor Edwards has received many teaching awards at the University of Florida. He was named Teacher of the Year in the College of Liberal Arts and Sciences in 1979, 1981, and 1990. He was both the Liberal Arts and Sciences Student Council Teacher of the Year and the University of Florida Honors Program Teacher of the Year in 1990. He was also selected by the alumni affairs office to be the Distinguished Alumni Professor for 1991–1993. The winners of this 2-year award are selected by graduates of the university. The Florida Section of the Mathematical Association of America awarded him the Distinguished Service Award in 1995 for his work in mathematics education for the state of Florida. Finally, his textbooks have been honored with various awards from the Text and Academic Authors Association.

Professor Edwards has been a frequent speaker at both research conferences and meetings of the National Council of Teachers of Mathematics. He has spoken on issues relating to the Advanced Placement calculus examination, especially the use of graphing calculators.

Professor Edwards is the author of the 2010 Great Course *Understanding Calculus: Problems, Solutions, and Tips*. This 36-lecture DVD course covers the content of the Advanced Placement AB calculus examination, which is equivalent to first-semester university calculus.

Professor Edwards has taught a wide range of mathematics courses at the University of Florida, from first-year calculus to graduate-level classes in algebra and numerical analysis. He particularly enjoys teaching calculus to freshman, due to the beauty of the subject and the enthusiasm of the students.

Table of Contents

Table of Contents

Table of Contents

Mathematics Describing the Real World: Precalculus and Trigonometry

Scope:

The goal of this course is for you to appreciate the beautiful and practical subject of precalculus. You will see how precalculus plays a fundamental role in all of science and engineering, as well as business and economics. As the name "precalculus" indicates, a thorough knowledge of this material is crucial for the study of calculus, and in my many years of teaching, I have found that success in calculus is assured if students have a strong background in precalculus.

The principal topics in precalculus are algebra and trigonometry. In fact, at many universities and high schools, the title of the course is Algebra and Trigonometry. However, precalculus covers much more: logarithms and exponents, systems of linear equations, matrices, conic sections, counting methods and probability, sequences and series, parametric equations, and polar coordinates. We will look at all these topics and their applications to real-world problems.

Our study of precalculus will be presented in the same order as a university-level precalculus course. The material is based on the 5th edition of the bestselling textbook *Precalculus: A Graphing Approach* by Ron Larson and Bruce H. Edwards (Houghton Mifflin, 2008). However, any standard precalculus textbook can be used for reference and support throughout the course. Please see the bibliography for an annotated list of appropriate supplementary textbooks.

We will begin our study of precalculus with a course overview and a brief look at functions. The concept of functions is fundamental in all of mathematics and will be a constant theme throughout the course. We will study all kinds of important and interesting functions: polynomial, rational, exponential, logarithmic, trigonometric, and parametric, to name a few.

As we progress through the course, most concepts will be introduced using illustrative examples. All the important theoretical ideas and theorems will be presented, but we will not dwell on their technical proofs. You will find that it is easy to understand and apply precalculus to real-world problems without knowing these theoretical intricacies.

Graphing calculators and computers are playing an increasing role in the mathematics classroom. Without a doubt, graphing technology can enhance the understanding of precalculus; hence, we will often use technology to verify and confirm our results.

You are encouraged to use all course materials to their maximum benefit, including the video lectures, which you can review as many times as you wish; the individual lecture summaries and accompanying problems in the workbook; and the supporting materials in the back of the workbook, such as the solutions to all problems, the glossary, and the review sheets of key theorems and formulas in algebra and trigonometry.

Good luck in your study of precalculus! I hope you enjoy these lectures as much as I did preparing them.

Introduction to Precalculus—Functions

Lesson 1

Topics

- Course overview.
- What is precalculus?
- Functions.
- Domain and range.
- What makes precalculus difficult?

Definitions and Properties

Note: Terms in bold correspond to entries in the Glossary or other appendixes.

- A **function**, f, from a set A to a set B is a relation that assigns to each element x in set A exactly one element y in set B. The notation is $y = f(x)$ where y is the value of the function at x.
- Set A is the **domain** of the function, or the set of inputs.
- The **range** is the set of all outputs, which is a subset of set B.
- The variable x is called the **independent variable** and $y = f(x)$ is the **dependent variable**.
- The **vertical line test** for functions states that if a vertical line intersects a graph at more than one point, then the graph is not of a function.

Summary

In this introductory lesson, we talk about the content, structure, and use of this precalculus course. We also turn to the study of functions, one of the most important concepts in all of mathematics.

Example 1: The Graph of a Function

Sketch the graph of the function $f(x) = 2x + 3$.

Solution

It is helpful to evaluate the function at a few numbers in the domain. For example,

$$f(2) = 7$$
$$f(0) = 3$$
$$f(-2) = -1$$

You can then plot these 3 points and connect them with a straight line, see figure 1.1.

2

Figure 1.1

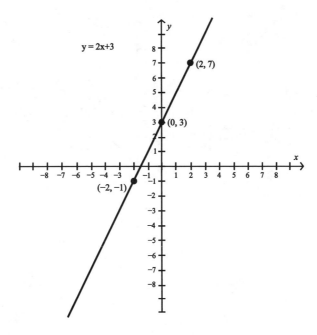

Example 2: The Graph of the Absolute Value Function

The **absolute value function** is defined as follows.

$$f(x) = |x| = \begin{cases} x, & x \geq 0 \\ -x, & x < 0 \end{cases}$$

Note: The absolute value of a number is always nonnegative.

The graph of the absolute value function looks like the letter V; it has a sharp corner at the origin, as in figure 1.2.

Figure 1.2

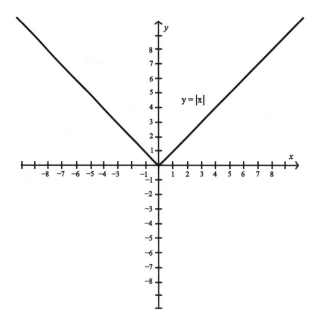

Example 3: An Application to Compound Interest

In this example, we use the letter t (time) for the independent variable. Suppose you invest $1000 in a bank account that pays 5% interest compounded annually. How much money will you have in the account after t years?

Solution

After the first year, you will have

$$1000 + 1000(0.05) = 1000(1 + 0.05) = 1000(1.05) = \$1050.$$

For the second year, you will earn 5% interest on the amount after the first year, as follows.

$$1000(1.05) + 1000(1.05)(0.05) = 1000(1.05)(1 + 0.05) = 1000(1.05)^2 = \$1102.50$$

Notice that you earned $50 interest the first year and $52.50 the second year. Continuing this pattern, you see that the amount in the bank after t years is given by $A(t) = 1000(1.05)^t$.

Study Tips

- To find the domain of a function, keep in mind that you cannot divide by zero, nor can you take square roots (or even roots) of negative numbers. In addition, in applications of precalculus, the domain might be limited by the context of the application.
- In general, it is more difficult to determine the range of a function than its domain.
- To analyze a function, it is often helpful to evaluate the function at a few numbers in order to get a feel for its behavior.
- If a vertical line intersects a graph at more than one point, then the graph is not of a function.
- Mathematics is not a spectator sport. Precalculus requires practice, so you will benefit from doing the problems at the end of each lesson. The worked-out solutions appear at the end of this workbook.

Pitfall

- Although we usually write $y = f(x)$ for a typical function, different letters are often used. The underlying concept is the same.

Problems

1. Evaluate the function $h(t) = t^2 - 2t$ at each specified value of the independent variable below and simplify.

    a. $h(2)$

    b. $h(1.5)$

    c. $h(x+2)$

2. Evaluate the function $q(x) = \dfrac{1}{x^2 - 9}$ at each specified value of the independent variable below and simplify.

    a. $q(0)$

    b. $q(3)$

    c. $q(y+3)$

3. Find the domain of the function $h(t) = \dfrac{4}{t}$.

4. Find the domain of the function $g(y) = \dfrac{y+2}{\sqrt{y-10}}$.

5. Determine whether the equation $x^2 + y^2 = 4$ represents y as a function of x.

6. Determine whether the equation $y = |4 - x|$ represents y as a function of x.

7. Write the area A of a circle as a function of its circumference C.

8. Sketch the graph of the following function by hand.

$$f(x) = \begin{cases} 2x + 3, & x < 0 \\ 3 - x, & x \geq 0 \end{cases}$$

9. Compare the graph of $y = \sqrt{x} + 2$ with the graph of $f(x) = \sqrt{x}$.

10. Compare the graph of $y = \sqrt{x - 2}$ with the graph of $f(x) = \sqrt{x}$.

Polynomial Functions and Zeros
Lesson 2

Topics

- Polynomial functions.
- Linear and quadratic functions.
- Zeros or roots of functions.
- The quadratic formula.
- Even and odd functions.
- The intermediate value theorem.

Definitions and Properties

- Let n be a nonnegative integer and let a_n, a_{n-1}, $\cdots$, a_2, a_1, a_0 be real numbers with $a_n \neq 0$. The function given by $f(x) = a_n x^n + a_{n-1} x^{n-1} + \cdots + a_2 x^2 + a_1 x + a_0$ is called a **polynomial function** in x of degree n, where a_n is the leading coefficient.
- A **linear polynomial** has the form $f(x) = a_1 x + a_0$ or $y = mx + b$.
- A **quadratic polynomial**, or parabola, has the form $f(x) = ax^2 + bx + c$, $a \neq 0$.
- A **zero**, or root, of a function $y = f(x)$ is a number a such that $f(a) = 0$.
- A function is **even** if $f(-x) = f(x)$. A function is **odd** if $f(-x) = -f(x)$.

Theorem and Formula

- The zeros of a quadratic function are given by the **quadratic formula**: $x = \dfrac{-b \pm \sqrt{b^2 - 4ac}}{2a}$.

- The **intermediate value theorem** says that if a and b are real numbers, $a < b$, and if f is a polynomial function such that $f(a) \neq f(b)$, then in the interval $[a, \, b]$, f takes on every value between $f(a)$ and $f(b)$. In particular, if $f(a)$ and $f(b)$ have opposite signs, then f has a zero in the interval $[a, \, b]$.

Summary

In this lesson, we study polynomial functions. The domain of a polynomial function consists of all real numbers and the graph is a smooth curve without any breaks or sharp corners. The graph of a polynomial function of degree 0 or 1 is a line of the form $y = mx + b$, with slope m and y-intercept b.

Example 1: The Graph of a Linear Polynomial

Sketch the graph of the first degree polynomial $f(x) = 3x - 5$.

Solution

The slope is 3, and the graph intercepts the y-axis at $(0, \ -5)$. Plotting some more points, you obtain the graph shown in figure 2.1.

Figure 2.1

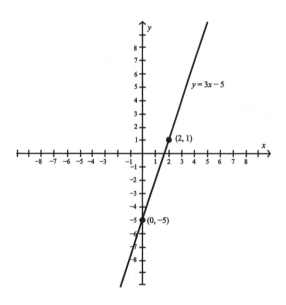

Example 2: Using the Quadratic Formula

Find the zeros of the quadratic polynomial $f(x) = 2x^2 + x - 3$.

Solution

We use the quadratic formula with $a = 2$, $b = 1$, and $c = -3$.

$$x = \frac{-b \pm \sqrt{b^2 - 4ac}}{2a} = \frac{-1 \pm \sqrt{(1)^2 - 4(2)(-3)}}{2(2)} = \frac{-1 \pm \sqrt{25}}{4} = \frac{-1 \pm 5}{4}$$

Thus, there are 2 zeros: $x = \dfrac{-1+5}{4} = 1$ and $x = \dfrac{-1-5}{4} = -\dfrac{3}{2}$.

If you graph this polynomial, you will see that the curve is a parabola that intersects the horizontal axis at 2 points, 1 and $-\dfrac{3}{2}$. However, if you apply the quadratic formula to the polynomial $f(x) = x^2 - 2x + \dfrac{13}{4}$, you obtain an expression involving the square root of a negative number. In that case, there are no real zeros.

Example 3: Locating Zeros

Use the intermediate value theorem to locate a zero of the function $f(x) = 3x^4 + 4x^3 - 3$.

Solution

Notice that $f(0) = -3$ and $f(1) = 4$. Therefore, there is a sign change on the interval $[0, 1]$. According to the intermediate value theorem, f must have a zero in this interval. Using a graphing utility (as shown in figure 2.2), you will see that the zero is approximately 0.779. In fact, there is a second zero, approximately -1.585.

Figure 2.2

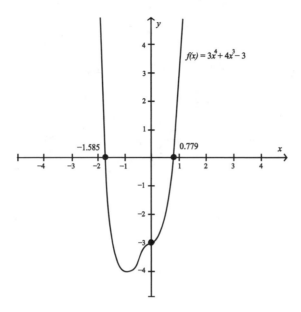

$f(x) = 3x^4 + 4x^3 - 3$

Study Tips

- Parallel lines have the same slope. The slopes of perpendicular lines are negative reciprocals of each other.
- The equation of a horizontal line is $y = c$, a constant. The equation of a vertical line is $x = c$.
- The real zeros of a function correspond to the points where the graph intersects the x-axis.
- Quadratic polynomials are often analyzed by completing the square.

Pitfalls

- If the quadratic formula yields the square root of a negative number, then the quadratic polynomial has no real roots.
- Finding the zeros of polynomials often requires factoring, which can be difficult.

Problems

1. Find the slope and y-intercept of the line $5x - y + 3 = 0$. Then sketch the line by hand.

2. Find an equation of the line with slope $m = 3$ and passing through the point $(0, -2)$.

3. Find the slope-intercept form of the line that passes through the points $(5, -1)$ and $(-5, 5)$.

4. Use factoring to solve the quadratic equation $x^2 + 4x = 12$.

5. Use the quadratic formula to solve the equation $2 + 2x - x^2 = 0$.

6. Solve the quadratic equation $x^2 + 4x - 32 = 0$ by completing the square.

7. Find 2 quadratic equations having the solutions -6 and 5.

8. Find a polynomial function that has zeros $4, -3, 3, 0$.

9. Use the intermediate value theorem and a graphing utility to find any intervals of length 1 in which the polynomial function $f(x) = x^3 - 3x^2 + 3$ is guaranteed to have a zero. Then use the zero or root feature of the graphing utility to approximate the real zeros of the function.

10. Find all solutions of the equation $5x^3 + 30x^2 + 45x = 0$.

11. Find all solutions of the equation $x^4 - 4x^2 + 3 = 0$.

12. Find 2 positive real numbers whose product is a maximum if the sum of the first number and twice the second number is 24.

Complex Numbers
Lesson 3

Topics

- The imaginary unit i.
- The set of complex numbers.
- Complex conjugates.
- Sums, products, and quotients of complex numbers.
- The fundamental theorem of algebra.
- Graphing complex numbers in the complex plane.
- Fractals and the Mandelbrot set.

Definitions and Properties

- The **imaginary unit i** is the $\sqrt{-1}$. In other words, $i^2 = -1$.
- A set of **complex numbers**, or **imaginary numbers**, consists of all numbers of the form $a + bi$, where a and b are real numbers.
- The **standard form** of a complex number is $a + bi$. If $b = 0$, then the number is real.
- The **complex conjugate** of $a + bi$ is $a - bi$.
- In the complex plane, the horizontal axis is the real axis and the vertical axis is the imaginary axis. A complex number $a + bi$ has coordinates (a, b).
- A complex number c is contained in the **Mandelbrot set** if and only if the following sequence is bounded: $c, c^2 + c, \left(c^2 + c\right)^2 + c, \left(\left(c^2 + c\right)^2 + c\right)^2 + c, \ \dots$.

Theorem

- The **fundamental theorem of algebra** says that if f is a polynomial of degree n, $n > 0$, then f has precisely n linear factors: $f(x) = a_n \left(x - c_1\right)\left(x - c_2\right)\cdots\left(x - c_n\right)$, where $c_1, c_2, \dots c_n$ are complex numbers.

Summary

In this lesson, we look at an extension of real numbers, called the set of complex numbers. Using complex numbers and the quadratic formula, we can now find the zeros of any quadratic polynomial.

Example 1: Using the Quadratic Formula

Find the zeros of the quadratic polynomial $f(x) = x^2 - 2x + \dfrac{13}{4}$.

Solution

We use the quadratic formula as follows.

$$x = \frac{-b \pm \sqrt{b^2 - 4ac}}{2a} = \frac{-(-2) \pm \sqrt{(-2)^2 - 4(1)\left(\dfrac{13}{4}\right)}}{2(1)} = \frac{2 \pm \sqrt{-9}}{2}$$

$$= \frac{2 \pm 3\sqrt{-1}}{2} = \frac{2 \pm 3i}{2} = 1 \pm \frac{3}{2}i$$

Thus, there are 2 complex zeros: $x = 1 + \dfrac{3}{2}i$ and $x = 1 - \dfrac{3}{2}i$.

Addition and multiplication of complex numbers are straightforward, as long as you replace i^2 with -1.

Example 2: Operations with Complex Numbers

The fundamental theorem of algebra states that in theory, all polynomials can be factored into linear factors. The zeros could be real or complex, and even repeated.

$$\sqrt{-9} = \sqrt{3^2(-1)} = 3\sqrt{-1} = 3i$$
$$(7 + 3i) + (7 - 3i) = 14$$
$$(2 - i)(4 + 3i) = 8 + 6i - 4i - 3i^2 = 11 + 2i$$

Example 3: Factoring Polynomials over the Complex Numbers

Factor the polynomial $f(x) = x^4 - x^2 - 20$.

Solution

We can first factor this fourth degree polynomial as the product of 2 quadratic polynomials. Then, we can factor each quadratic.

$$x^4 - x^2 - 20 = \left(x^2 - 5\right)\left(x^2 + 4\right)$$
$$= \left(x + \sqrt{5}\right)\left(x - \sqrt{5}\right)\left(x^2 + 4\right)$$
$$= \left(x + \sqrt{5}\right)\left(x - \sqrt{5}\right)\left(x + 2i\right)\left(x - 2i\right)$$

There are 4 zeros: $\pm\sqrt{5}$, $\pm 2i$. Notice that the complex zeros occur as conjugate pairs.

Example 4: The Mandelbrot Set

Fractals are a relatively new and exciting area of mathematics. The famous Mandelbrot set is defined using sequences of complex numbers. The complex number $c = i$ is in the Mandelbrot set because the following sequence is bounded.

$$c = i$$
$$i^2 + i = -1 + i$$
$$\left(-1 + i\right)^2 + i = -i$$
$$\left(-i\right)^2 + i = -1 + i$$
$$\text{etc.}$$

On the other hand, the complex number $1 + i$ is not in the Mandelbrot set.

Study Tips

- The sum of a complex number and its conjugate is a real number. Furthermore, the product of a complex number and its conjugate is a real number.
- Complex zeros of polynomials having real coefficients occur in conjugate pairs.

Pitfall

- Some of the familiar laws of radicals for real numbers do not hold with complex numbers. For example, the square root of a product is not necessarily the product of the square roots: $\sqrt{-4}\sqrt{-9} = (2i)(3i) = -6$, whereas $\sqrt{(-4)(-9)} = \sqrt{36} = 6$.

1. Simplify $13i - (14 - 7i)$.

2. Simplify $\sqrt{-6}\sqrt{-2}$.

3. Simplify $(1+i)(3-2i)$.

4. Simplify $4i(8+5i)$.

5. Write the complex conjugate of the complex number $4+3i$, then multiply by its complex conjugate.

6. Write the complex conjugate of the complex number $3-\sqrt{-2}$, then multiply by its complex conjugate.

7. Write the quotient in standard form: $\dfrac{2}{4-5i}$.

8. Find all zeros of the function $f(x) = x^2 - 12x + 26$, and write the polynomial as a product of linear factors.

9. Find all zeros of the function $f(x) = x^4 + 10x^2 + 9$, and write the polynomial as a product of linear factors.

10. Find a polynomial function with real coefficients that has zeros 2, 2, $4-i$.

11. For $c = \dfrac{1}{2}i$, find the first 4 terms of the sequence given by

$$c, \ c^2 + c, \ \left(c^2 + c\right) + c, \ \left[\left(c^2 + c\right) + c\right] + c, \ \ldots \ .$$

From the terms, do you think the number is in the Mandelbrot set?

Rational Functions

Lesson 4

Topics

- Rational functions.
- Horizontal and vertical asymptotes.

Definitions and Properties

- A **rational function** can be written in the form $f(x) = \dfrac{N(x)}{D(x)}$, where $N(x)$ and $D(x)$ are polynomials.
- The domain of a rational function consists of all values of x such that the denominator is not zero.
- The vertical line $x = a$ is a **vertical asymptote** of the graph of f if $f(x) \to \infty$ or $f(x) \to -\infty$ as $x \to a$, either from the right or from the left.
- The horizontal line $y = b$ is a **horizontal asymptote** of the graph of f if $f(x) \to b$ as $x \to \infty$ or $x \to -\infty$.

Test for Horizontal Asympotes

Let $f(x) = \dfrac{N(x)}{D(x)}$ be a rational function.

- If the degree of the numerator is less than the degree of the denominator, then $y = 0$ is a horizontal asymptote.

- If the degree of the numerator equals the degree of the denominator, then the horizontal asymptote is the ratio of the leading coefficients.

- If the degree of the numerator is greater than the degree of the denominator, then there is no horizontal asymptote.

Summary

In this lesson, we look at a class of functions called rational functions, which are quotients of polynomials. Many rational functions have vertical and/or horizontal asymptotes.

Example 1: Finding Asymptotes

Find the vertical and horizontal asymptotes of the graph of the rational function $f(x) = \dfrac{2x^2}{x^2 - 1}$.

Solution

From figure 4.1, you see that the horizontal asymptote is $y = 2$. The vertical asymptotes are $x = \pm 1$ because these are zeros of the denominator, while not of the numerator.

Figure 4.1

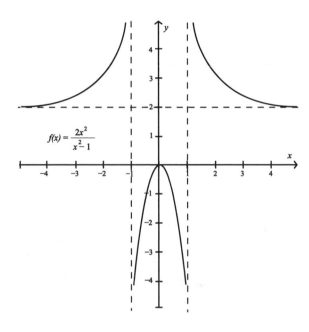

$$f(x) = \frac{2x^2}{x^2 - 1}$$

Example 2: Finding Asymptotes and Holes

You have to be careful when finding vertical asymptotes. Find the vertical asymptotes of the graph of the function $f(x) = \dfrac{x^2 + x - 2}{(x+2)(x-3)}$.

Solution

It is not sufficient to assume that the vertical asymptotes are simply the zeros of the denominator. You need to factor the numerator and cancel the common factor.

$$f(x) = \frac{x^2 + x - 2}{(x+2)(x-3)} = \frac{(x+2)(x-1)}{(x+2)(x-3)} = \frac{(x-1)}{(x-3)}, \ x \neq -2$$

Hence, the only vertical asymptote is $x = 3$, whereas the graph has a hole at $x = -2$, shown in figure 4.2.

Figure 4.2

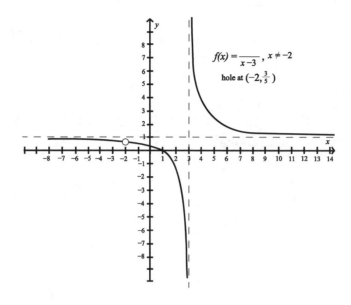

$$f(x) = \frac{}{x-3}, \ x \neq -2$$

hole at $\left(-2, \frac{3}{5}\right)$

Example 3: The Design of a School Poster

This example illustrates how rational functions arise in real-life applications. Suppose you want to design a school poster having 48 square inches of print. The margins on each side of the page are 1½ inches wide. The margins at the top and bottom are each 1 inch deep. What should the dimensions of the page be so that the minimum amount of paper is used?

Solution

Label a diagram as seen in figure 4.3.

Figure 4.3

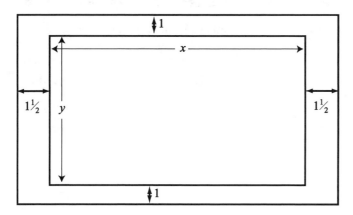

If x and y are the dimensions inside the margins, then $xy = 48$ or $y = \dfrac{48}{x}$. The area to be minimized is

$$A = (x+3)(y+2)$$
$$= (x+3)\left(\dfrac{48}{x} + 2\right)$$
$$= \dfrac{(x+3)(48+2x)}{x}.$$

Using a graphic utility, graph this rational function and estimate the minimum value. You obtain $x \approx 8.5$. Hence, $y \approx \dfrac{48}{8.5} \approx 5.6$. The dimensions for the entire page are $x+3 \approx 11.5$ inches by $y+2 \approx 7.6$ inches. It is interesting to note that by using calculus you can find the exact value $x = 6\sqrt{2}$.

Study Tips

- A graphing calculator is useful in verifying the shape and asymptotes of the graph of a rational function.
- A rational function has a finite number of vertical asymptotes.
- A rational function can have zero or one horizontal asymptote.
- Some graphing utilities have difficulty graphing rational functions that have vertical asymptotes. Often, the utility will connect parts of the graph that are not supposed to be connected. To eliminate this, try changing the mode form to *dot* mode.

Pitfalls

- You cannot assume that the vertical asymptotes are the zeros of the denominator. You must check that these zeros are not zeros of the numerator as well.
- It is possible for a nonrational function to have 2 horizontal asymptotes, one to the right and one to the left.
- It is possible for a nonrational function to have an infinite number of vertical asymptotes. We will see such an example when we study the tangent function in trigonometry.

1. Sketch the graph of the following rational function, indicating any intercepts and asymptotes.

   a. $f(x) = \dfrac{1}{x+2}$

   b. $f(x) = \dfrac{1}{x-6}$

   c. $f(x) = \dfrac{x^2}{x^2-4}$

   d. $f(x) = \dfrac{x^2+3x}{x^2+x-6}$

2. Identify any horizontal and vertical asymptotes of the following functions

   a. $f(x) = \dfrac{1}{x^2}$.

   b. $f(x) = \dfrac{x^2-25}{x^2+5x}$.

3. Find the zeros of the rational function $f(x) = \dfrac{x^2-4}{x+3}$.

4. Write a rational function f having a vertical asymptote $x = 2$, a horizontal asymptote $y = 0$, and a zero at $x = 1$.

5. Using a graphing utility, graph the following functions and indicate any asymptotes.

   a. $h(x) = \dfrac{6x}{\sqrt{x^2+1}}$

   b. $g(x) = \dfrac{4|x-2|}{x+1}$

Inverse Functions
Lesson 5

Topics

- Combinations of functions.
- Inverse functions.
- Graphs of inverse functions.
- One-to-one functions and the horizontal line test.
- Finding inverse functions.

Definitions and Properties

- **Addition** and **multiplication** of functions is defined by:

$$(f + g)(x) = f(x) + g(x)$$
$$(fg)(x) = f(x)g(x).$$

- The **composition** of 2 functions is defined by $(f \circ g)(x) = f(g(x))$.
- Let f and g be 2 functions such that $f(g(x)) = x$ for all x in the domain of g, and $g(f(x)) = x$ for all x in the domain of f. Then g is the **inverse** of f, denoted f^{-1}.
- If a function has an inverse, then the inverse is unique. If f is the inverse of g, then g is the inverse of f. The domain of f is the range of g, and the domain of g is the range of f.
- The graphs of inverse functions are symmetric across the line $y = x$.
- A function is **one-to-one** if, for a and b in the domain, $f(a) = f(b)$ implies $a = b$. A function has an inverse if and only if it is one-to-one.
- A function is one-to-one if its graph passes the **horizontal line test**: Every horizontal line intersects the graph at most once.

Summary

You can combine functions in many ways, including addition, multiplication, and composition. In particular, inverse functions, such as $f(x) = 5x$ and $g(x) = \dfrac{x}{5}$, satisfy $f(g(x)) = x$ and $g(f(x)) = x$.

Example 1: Verifying Inverse Functions Algebraically

The functions $f(x) = 2x^3 - 1$ and $g(x) = \sqrt[3]{\dfrac{x+1}{2}}$ are inverses of each other because

$$f(g(x)) = f\left(\sqrt[3]{\frac{x+1}{2}}\right) = 2\left(\sqrt[3]{\frac{x+1}{2}}\right)^3 - 1 = 2\left(\frac{x+1}{2}\right) - 1 = (x+1) - 1 = x,$$

and similarly, $g(f(x)) = x$. Notice that the graph of g is a reflection of the graph of f in the line $y = x$ (figure 5.1).

Figure 5.1

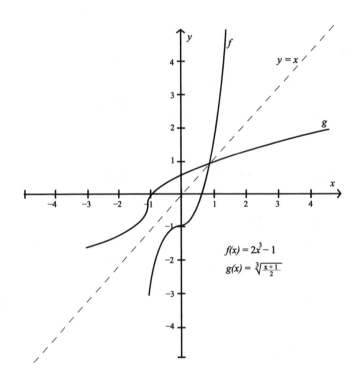

$$f(x) = 2x^3 - 1$$
$$g(x) = \sqrt[3]{\frac{x+1}{2}}$$

Example 2: Finding Inverse Functions

If a function is one-to-one, then it has an inverse. To illustrate a technique for finding the inverse function, find the inverse function of $f(x) = \sqrt{x} + 1$.

Solution

Begin with the equation $y = \sqrt{x} + 1$, interchange the roles of x and y, and solve for y.

$$y = \sqrt{x} + 1, \ x \geq 0, \ y \geq 1$$
$$x = \sqrt{y} + 1$$
$$x - 1 = \sqrt{y}$$
$$y = (x-1)^2, \ x \geq 1, \ y \geq 0$$
$$f^{-1}(x) = (x-1)^2, \ x \geq 1, \ y \geq 0$$

Notice how the domains and ranges have been interchanged.

Example 3: Temperature Scales

Inverse relationships can arise in applications. The Fahrenheit (F) and Celsius (C) temperature scales are related by 2 equivalent formulas: $F = \dfrac{9}{5}C + 32$ and $C = \dfrac{5}{9}(F - 32)$. If the temperature is C = 35° on the Celsius scale, then the corresponding Fahrenheit temperature is $F = \dfrac{9}{5}(35) + 32 = 63 + 32 = 95°$.

Study Tips

- Inverse functions satisfy the equations $f\left(f^{-1}(x)\right) = x$ and $f^{-1}\left(f(x)\right) = x$.
- Graphically, if (a, b) is a point on the graph of the function f, then (b, a) is on the graph of the inverse.

Pitfalls

- The notation for an inverse function can be misleading. f^{-1} does not mean the reciprocal of f, $\dfrac{1}{f}$.

- A function must be one-to-one in order to have an inverse. For example, the function $f(x) = x^2$ does not have an inverse because the parabola does not pass the horizontal line test. However, if you restrict the domain to $x \geq 0$, then the inverse exists: $f^{-1}(x) = \sqrt{x}$.

- In general, the composition of functions is not commutative. That is, in general, $(f \circ g) \neq (g \circ f)$.

1. Let $f(x) = x^2 + 5$ and $g(x) = \sqrt{1-x}$. Find the following.

   a. $(f + g)(x)$

   b. $(f - g)(x)$

   c. $(fg)(x)$

   d. $\left(\dfrac{f}{g}\right)(x)$

2. Let $f(x) = \sqrt{x+4}$ and $g(x) = x^2$. Determine the domains of the following.

   a. f

   b. g

   c. $f \circ g$

3. Find the inverse of the function $f(x) = 6x$.

4. Find the inverse of the function $f(x) = x - 3$.

5. Show that the functions $f(x) = x^3 + 5$ and $g(x) = \sqrt[3]{x-5}$ are inverses of each other.

6. Determine whether the function $f(x) = \dfrac{1}{x^2}$ is one-to-one.

7. Determine whether the function $f(x) = \sqrt{2x+3}$ is one-to-one.

8. Find the inverse function of $f(x) = 2x - 3$. Describe the relationship between the graphs of f and its inverse.

9. Find the inverse function of $f(x) = \sqrt{4 - x^2}$, $0 \leq x \leq 2$. Describe the relationship between the graphs of f and its inverse.

10. Restrict the domain of the function $f(x) = |x + 2|$ so that the function is one-to-one and has an inverse. Then find the inverse function f^{-1}. State the domains and ranges of f and f^{-1}.

Solving Inequalities

Lesson 6

Topics

- Interval notation.
- Properties of inequalities.
- Inequalities involving absolute values.

Interval Notation

- **Closed interval** $[a,\ b]$ means $a \leq x \leq b$.
- **Open interval** $(a,\ b)$ means $a < x < b$.
- **Infinite interval** $[a,\ \infty)$ means $x \geq a$.
- **Infinite interval** $(-\infty,\ b)$ means $x < b$.

Properties of Inequalities

- $a < b$ and $b < c$ implies $a < c$ (transitivity).

- $a < b$ and $c < d$ implies $a + c < b + d$.

- $a < b$ implies $a + c < b + c$.

- $a < b$ and $c > 0$ implies $ac < bc$.

- $a < b$ and $c < 0$ implies $ac > bc$.

- Let $a > 0$. Then

    o $|x| < a$ if and only if $-a < x < a$.

    o $|x| > a$ if and only if $x < -a$ or $x > a$.

Summary

We have already used inequalities throughout these lessons, especially when studying domains of functions. We see how the properties of inequalities are used in solving the following examples.

Example 1: Solving an Inequality

Solve the inequality $1 - \frac{3}{2}x \geq x - 4$.

Solution

Notice how the inequality is reversed when you divide by -5.

$$1 - \frac{3}{2}x \geq x - 4$$
$$2 - 3x \geq 2x - 8$$
$$2 - 5x \geq -8$$
$$-5x \geq -10$$
$$x \leq \frac{-10}{-5}$$
$$x \leq 2$$

Example 2: Solving an Inequality Involving Absolute Values

Inequalities involving absolute values occur frequently in calculus. Solve the inequality $|x-5| \leq 2$.

Solution

$$|x-5| \leq 2$$
$$-2 \leq x - 5 \leq 2$$
$$3 \leq x \leq 7$$

The solution consists of all real numbers in the closed interval $[3,\ 7]$. If the problem had asked for the solution to $|x-5| > 2$, then the solution set would be all numbers less than 3 or greater than 7 $(-\infty,\ 3) \cup (7,\ \infty)$.

Example 3: An Application of Inequalities

Inequalities can arise in applications. If a student has scored 68 and 77 on 2 tests, what must the student score on the third test to bring the average up to 80?

Solution

Let x be the score on the third test. The average of the 3 scores must be greater than or equal to 80.

$$\frac{68 + 77 + x}{3} \geq 80$$
$$145 + x \geq 3(80) = 240$$
$$x \geq 240 - 145 = 95$$

The student needs at least a score of 95 on the third test.

Study Tips

- The set theory expression $A \cup B$ means the set of all numbers in the set A together with all the numbers in the set B. The symbol $\cup$ is called the **union symbol**.
- The set theory expression $A \cap B$ means all numbers that are contained in both sets A and B. The symbol $\cap$ is called the **intersection symbol**.
- The set of all real numbers can be expressed as $(-\infty, \infty)$.
- The horizontal line over an answer indicates a **recurring number**: $0.\overline{9} = 0.9999999...$.

Pitfalls

- Infinity (∞) is not a number. You should not write infinite intervals using a bracket next to the infinity symbol. That is, write $[-4, \infty)$ not $[-4, \infty]$.

- If you multiply or divide both sides of an inequality by a negative number, you must reverse the inequality.

- It is incorrect to write an inequality in the form $7 < x < 3$. There are no values of x that are greater than 7 and also less than 3.

Problems

1. Find the domain of the following functions.

    a. $f(x) = \sqrt{x - 5}$.

    b. $f(x) = \sqrt{x^2 - 4}$.

2. Solve the following inequalities.

a. $-10x < 40.$

b. $4(x+1) < 2x+3.$

c. $-8 \leq 1-3(x-2) < 13.$

d. $0 \leq \dfrac{x+3}{2} < 5.$

e. $|x-7| < 6.$

f. $|x+14|+3 > 17.$

3. Determine the intervals on which the polynomial $x^2 - 4x - 5$ is entirely negative and those on which it is entirely positive.

4. Use absolute value notation to describe the set of all real numbers that lie within 10 units of 7.

5. Use absolute value notation to describe the set of all real numbers that are at least 5 units from 3.

Exponential Functions

Lesson 7

Topics

- Exponential functions.
- Review of exponents.
- Graphs of exponential functions.
- The natural base e.
- The natural exponential function.

Definitions and Properties

- The **exponential function** f with base a ($a > 0$, $a \neq 1$) is defined $f(x) = a^x$, where x is any real number.
- The domain of the exponential function is $(-\infty, \infty)$, and the range is $(0, \infty)$. The exponential function is increasing if $a > 0$ and decreasing if $0 < a < 1$. The intercept is $(0, 1)$. The x-axis is the horizontal asymptote.
- The exponential function is one-to-one and hence has an inverse (the logarithmic function, to be defined in the next lesson).
- The **natural base** $e \approx 2.71828$ is the most important base in calculus. The corresponding function $f(x) = e^x$ is called the **natural exponential function**.

Properties of Exponents

Let a, b be real numbers and m, n integers.

- $a^m a^n = a^{m+n}$, $\dfrac{a^m}{a^n} = a^{m-n}$

- $a^{-n} = \dfrac{1}{a^n}$, $a^0 = 1$ ($a \neq 0$), $\left| a^2 \right| = |a|^2 = a^2$

- $(ab)^m = a^m b^m$, $\left(\dfrac{a}{b} \right)^m = \dfrac{a^m}{b^m}$

- $\left(a^m \right)^n = a^{mn}$

Formulas for Compound Interest

After t years, the balance A in an account with principle P and annual interest rate r (in decimal form) is given by the following.

- For n compounding per year: $A = P\left(1 + \dfrac{r}{n}\right)^{nt}$.

- For continuous compounding: $A = Pe^{rt}$.

Summary

In the next block of lessons, we define and explore exponential and logarithmic functions. The exponential function is defined for all real numbers. You can graph an exponential function by plotting points or using a graphing utility.

Example 1: The Graph of an Exponential Function

Graph the exponential function $f(x) = 2^x$.

Solution

Plot the following ordered pairs and connect them with a smooth curve: $(3,\, 8)$, $(2,\, 4)$, $(1,\, 2)$, $(0,\, 1)$, $\left(-1,\, \frac{1}{2}\right)$, $\left(-2,\, \frac{1}{4}\right)$. Note that the resulting graph is continuous and passes the horizontal line test, see figure 7.1.

Figure 7.1

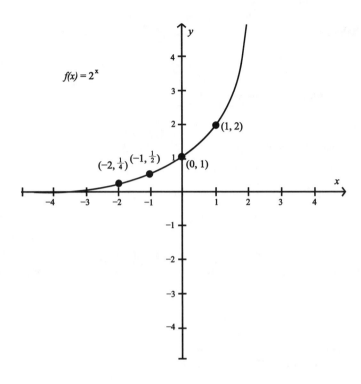

Example 2: A Model for Radioactive Decay

An exponential function to base 2 can be used to model radioactive decay. Let y represent a mass, in grams, of radioactive strontium 90, whose half-life is 29 years. The quantity of strontium present after t years is given by

$$y = 10\left(\frac{1}{2}\right)^{t/29}.$$

Try graphing the model on your graphing utility to verify the results of the example. Notice that the graph is decreasing.

    a. According to this model, what is the initial mass?

    b. How much strontium is present after 29 years?

    c. How much is present after 80 years?

Solution

a.   Letting $t = 0$, you see that the initial mass is $y = 10 \left(\dfrac{1}{2} \right)^{0/29} = 10 \left(\dfrac{1}{2} \right)^{0} = 10(1) = 10$ grams.

b.   Letting $t = 29$, you see that half the amount remains: $y = 10 \left(\dfrac{1}{2} \right)^{29/29} = 10 \left(\dfrac{1}{2} \right)^{1} = 5$ grams.

The solution to this part illustrates that the half-life is 29 years.

c.   When $t = 80$, you need a calculator to obtain $y = 10 \left(\dfrac{1}{2} \right)^{80/29} \approx 1.48$ grams.

Example 3: An Application to Compound Interest

We can apply exponential functions to compound interest. A total of $12,000 is invested at an annual interest rate of 3%. Find the balance after 4 years if the interest is compounded

a.   quarterly, and

b.   continuously.

Solution

We use a calculator for both calculations.

a. $A = P \left(1 + \dfrac{r}{n} \right)^{nt} = 12,000 \left(1 + \dfrac{.03}{4} \right)^{4(4)} \approx \$13,523.91$

b. $A = Pe^{rt} = 12,000 e^{0.03(4)} \approx \$13,529.96$

Notice that the account has earned slightly more interest under continuous compounding.

Study Tips

- The base of the exponential function must be positive because a^x is undefined for certain negative values of x. Similarly, the base cannot be 1 because $f(x) = 1^x = 1$ is a linear function.

- The number e can be defined as the limit as x tends to infinity of the expression $\left(1+\dfrac{1}{x}\right)^x$.

  In calculus, this is written $\displaystyle\lim_{x\to\infty}\left(1+\dfrac{1}{x}\right)^x = e.$

Pitfall

- The tower of exponents a^{b^c} means $a^{\left(b^c\right)}$ not $\left(a^b\right)^c$.

Problems

1. Evaluate the expressions.

   a. $4^2(3)$

   b. $3(3^3)$

2. Evaluate the expressions.

   a. $\dfrac{3}{3^{-4}}$

   b. $24(-2)^{-5}$

3. Graph the following exponential functions by hand. Identify any asymptotes and intercepts, and determine whether the graph of the function is increasing or decreasing.

   a. $f(x)=5^x$

   b. $f(x)=5^{-x}$

4. Use the graph of $f(x)=3^x$ to describe the transformation that yields the graph of $g(x)=3^{x-5}$.

5. Use the graph of $f(x)=0.3^x$ to describe the transformation that yields the graph of $g(x)=-0.3^x+5$.

6. Use a calculator to evaluate the function $f(x)=50e^{4x}$ for $x=0.02$. Round your result to the nearest thousandth.

7. Graph the following functions by hand. Identify any asymptotes and intercepts, and determine whether the graph of the function is increasing or decreasing.

    a. $f(x) = e^{-x}$

    b. $f(x) = 2 + e^{x-5}$

8. Determine the balance for $2500 dollars invested at 2.5% interest if

    a. interest is compounded annually,

    b. interest is compounded daily, and

    c. interest is compounded continuously.

Logarithmic Functions
Lesson 8

Topics

- Logarithmic functions.
- Common logarithms and natural logarithms.
- Properties of logarithms.
- Graphs of logarithmic functions.
- The rule of 70.

Definitions and Properties

- The **logarithmic function** f with base a ($a > 0$, $a \neq 1$) is defined by $y = \log_a x$ if and only if $x = a^y$. Logarithms to base 10 are called **common logarithms**.
- The domain of the logarithmic function is $(0, \infty)$, and the range is $(-\infty, \infty)$. The logarithmic function is increasing if $a > 0$ and decreasing if $0 < a < 1$. The intercept is $(1, 0)$. The y-axis is the vertical asymptote.
- The logarithmic function is one-to-one, and the inverse is the exponential function.
- The graphs of the logarithmic and exponential functions (with the same base) are reflections of each other across the line $y = x$.
- The **natural logarithmic function** is the inverse of the natural exponential function: $y = \log_e x$ if and only if $x = e^y$. The usual notation is $y = \ln x$.

The Rule of 70

The doubling time for a deposit earning $r\%$ interest compounded *continuously* is approximately $\dfrac{70}{r}$ years.

Properties of Logarithms

- $\log_a 1 = 0$

- $\log_a a = 1$

- $\log_a a^x = x$

- $a^{\log_a x} = x$

- If $\log_a x = \log_a y$, then $x = y$.

Summary

The inverse of the one-to-one exponential function is the logarithmic function. You can calculate logarithms by referring back to the corresponding exponential function.

Example 1: Calculating Logarithms

- $\log_2(32) = 5$ because $2^5 = 32$.

- $\log_3(1) = 0$ because $3^0 = 1$.

- $\log_4(2) = \dfrac{1}{2}$ because $4^{1/2} = 2$.

- $\log_{10}(1000) = 3$ because $10^3 = 1000$.

The graph of the logarithmic function $y = \log_a x$ is a reflection of the graph of the exponential function $y = a^x$ about the line $y = x$. It is easy to graph horizontal and vertical shifts of logarithmic functions.

Example 2: Graphing Logarithmic Functions

Graph and compare the functions $g(x) = \log_{10} x$ and $f(x) = \log_{10}(x - 1)$.

Solution

The graph of f is the graph of g shifted one unit to the right (figure 8.1). The intercept for f is $(2,\ 0)$, and the vertical asymptote is $x = 1$.

Figure 8.1

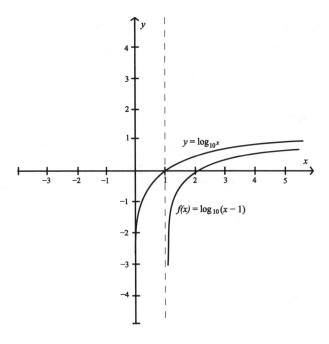

Example 3: Calculating Natural Logarithms

The natural logarithmic function is the inverse of the natural exponential function.

- $\ln \dfrac{1}{e} = \ln e^{-1} = -1$

- $e^{\ln 5} = 5$

- $4\ln 1 = 4(0) = 0$

- $2\ln e = 2(1) = 2$

Study Tips

- Calculators generally have 2 logarithm buttons: base 10 (common logarithm) and base e (natural logarithm).
- It is helpful to remember that logarithms are exponents.
- The domain of the logarithmic function is the range of the corresponding exponential function. Similarly, the range of the logarithmic function is the domain of the exponential function.

Pitfall

- You cannot evaluate the logarithm of zero or a negative number.

Problems

1. Write the following logarithmic equations in exponential form.

   a. $\log_4 64 = 3$

   b. $\log_{32} 4 = \dfrac{2}{5}$

2. Evaluate the function $f(x) = \log_2 x$ at $x = 16$.

3. Evaluate the function $f(x) = \log_{10} x$ at $x = \dfrac{1}{1000}$.

4. Use a calculator to evaluate $\log_{10} 345$. Round your answer to 3 decimal places.

5. Use a calculator to evaluate $\ln \sqrt{42}$. Round your answer to 3 decimal places.

6. Solve the equation for x: $\log_6 6^2 = x$.

7. Sketch the graph of $f(x) = 3^x$, and use the graph to sketch the graph of $g(x) = \log_3 x$.

8. Find the domain, vertical asymptote, and x-intercept of the following logarithmic functions. Then sketch the graphs by hand.

   a. $f(x) = \log_2 (x+2)$.

   b. $f(x) = \ln(x+1)$.

   c. $f(x) = \ln(-x)$.

Properties of Logarithms

Lesson 9

Topics

- The change of base formula.
- Logarithms of products, quotients, and powers.
- Applications of logarithms.

Theorems and Properties

- The **change of base formula** is $\log_a x = \dfrac{\log_{10} x}{\log_{10} a} = \dfrac{\ln x}{\ln a}$.

- $\log_a(uv) = \log_a u + \log_a v$

- $\log_a\left(\dfrac{u}{v}\right) = \log_a u - \log_a v$

- $\log_a u^n = n \log_a u$

The Rule of 72

The doubling time for a deposit earning $r\,\%$ interest compounded *annually* is $\dfrac{72}{r}$ years.

Summary

Graphing calculators usually have only 2 keys for logarithms, those to base 10 and the natural logarithm. To calculate logarithms to other bases, use the change of base formula.

Example 1: Calculating Logarithms

- $\log_4(25) = \dfrac{\log_{10} 25}{\log_{10} 4} \approx \dfrac{1.39794}{0.60206} \approx 2.32$

- $\log_4(25) = \dfrac{\ln 25}{\ln 4} \approx \dfrac{3.21888}{1.38629} \approx 2.32$

Notice that the 2 answers agree.

Example 2: Simplifying Logarithms

One of the most important properties of logarithms is that the logarithms of products are the sums of the logarithms. Similarly, the logarithms of quotients are the differences of the logarithms.

- $\ln 2 + \ln 3 = \ln\left[(2)(3)\right] = \ln 6$

- $\ln \dfrac{2}{27} = \ln 2 - \ln 27$

- $\log_{10} 49 = \log_{10}\left(7^2\right) = 2\log_{10} 7$

Example 3: Writing a Product as a Sum

Logarithms play a major role in calculus by converting products to sums.

- $\log_4\left(5x^3 y\right) = \log_4 5 + \log_4 x^3 + \log_4 y = \log_4 5 + 3\log_4 x + \log_4 y$

- $\ln \dfrac{\sqrt{3x-5}}{7} = \ln\left[\dfrac{(3x-5)^{\frac{1}{2}}}{7}\right] = \ln(3x-5)^{\frac{1}{2}} - \ln 7 = \dfrac{1}{2}\ln(3x-5) - \ln 7$

Example 4: The Rule of 72

The rule of 72 is a convenient tool for estimating the doubling time for an investment earning interest compounded annually. Suppose a bank pays 8% interest, compounded annually. Use the rule of 72 to approximate the doubling time.

Solution

The rule of 72 says that the doubling time is approximately $\dfrac{72}{8} = 9$ years. If you use the formula for compound interest, you will see that this approximation is excellent.

- Calculators generally have 2 buttons for logarithms: base 10 (common logarithm) and base e (natural logarithm). Use the change of base formula for other bases.
- The rule of 72 is for compound interest, as contrasted with the rule of 70 for continuous compounding.

Pitfalls

- There is no formula for the logarithm of a sum or difference. In particular, $\log_a(u+v) \neq \log_a u + \log_a v$.

- Be careful of domain changes when using properties of logarithms. For example, the domain of $y = \ln x^2$ is all $x \neq 0$, whereas the domain of $y = 2\ln x$ is all $x > 0$.

- The notation for logarithms can be confusing. Note that $(\ln x)^n \neq n\ln x$.

Problems

1. Evaluate the following logarithms using the change of base formula. Round your answer to 3 decimal places.

   a. $\log_3 7$

   b. $\log_{15} 1460$

2. Rewrite the following expressions in terms of $\ln 4$ and $\ln 5$.

   a. $\ln 20$

   b. $\ln \dfrac{5}{64}$

3. Use the properties of logarithms to rewrite and simplify the following logarithmic expressions

   a. $\log_4 8$.

   b. $\ln\left(5e^6\right)$.

4. Use the properties of logarithms to expand the expression $\ln\sqrt{z}$ as a sum, difference, and/or constant multiple of logarithms.

5. Condense the expression $\ln x - 3\ln(x+1)$ to the logarithm of a single quantity.

6. Find the exact value of $\log_3 9$ without using a calculator.

7. Find the exact value of $\ln e^3 - \ln e^7$ without using a calculator.

Exponential and Logarithmic Equations

Lesson 10

Topics

- Equations involving logarithms and exponents.
- Approximate solutions.
- Applications.

Summary

In this lesson, we solve a variety of equations involving logarithms and exponents.

Example 1: Solving an Exponential Equation

Solve the equation $4e^{2x} - 3 = 2$.

Solution

We use the properties of logarithms and exponents to solve for x.

$$4e^{2x} - 3 = 2$$

$$4e^{2x} = 5$$

$$e^{2x} = \frac{5}{4}$$

$$\ln e^{2x} = \ln\left(\frac{5}{4}\right)$$

$$2x = \ln\left(\frac{5}{4}\right)$$

$$x = \frac{1}{2}\ln\left(\frac{5}{4}\right) \approx 0.11$$

Example 2: Solving a Logarithmic Equation

You should be careful to check your answers after solving an equation. In this example, you will see that one of the "solutions" is not valid. The appearance of these "extraneous" solutions occurs frequently with logarithmic equations because the domain of the logarithmic function is restricted to positive real numbers.

Solve the equation $\ln(x-2)+\ln(2x-3)=2\ln x$.

Solution

Notice how we use the properties of logarithms to simplify both sides and remove the logarithms.

$$\ln(x-2)+\ln(2x-3)=2\ln x$$
$$\ln\left[(x-2)(2x-3)\right]=\ln x^2$$
$$(x-2)(2x-3)=x^2$$
$$2x^2-7x+6=x^2$$
$$x^2-7x+6=0$$
$$(x-6)(x-1)=0$$

There are 2 solutions to this quadratic equation: $x=1$ and $x=6$. However, $x=1$ is an extraneous solution because it is not in the domain of the original expression. Therefore, the only solution is $x=6$.

Example 3: Approximating the Solution of an Equation

In this example, we are forced to use a computer or graphing calculator to approximate the solution of the equation. Approximate the solution to the equation $\ln x = x^2 - 2$.

Solution

Write the equation as a function: $f(x)=\ln x - x^2 + 2$. The zeros of this function are the solutions to the original equation. Using a graphing utility, you see that the graph has 2 zeros, approximately 0.138 and 1.564. Note that it is impossible to find the exact solutions to the equation.

Study Tips

- There many ways to write an answer. For instance, in the first example, you could have written the answer as $\frac{1}{2}\ln\left(\frac{5}{4}\right)$, $\ln\left(\frac{5}{4}\right)^{\frac{1}{2}}$, $\ln\sqrt{\frac{5}{4}}$, $\ln\frac{\sqrt{5}}{2}$, or $\frac{1}{2}\left[\ln 5 - \ln 4\right]$. All of these are correct.
- Recall that the logarithm of a sum is not the sum of the logarithms. That is, the equation $\log_{10}(x+10) \neq \log_{10} x + \log_{10} 10$ for all values of x. However, you can show that this equation does have a solution: $x = \frac{10}{9}$.

Pitfalls

- It's important to distinguish between exact and approximate answers. For instance, the exact answer to the equation $5 + 2 \ln x = 4$ is $x = e^{-1/2} = \dfrac{1}{\sqrt{e}}$. This is approximately equal to 0.61, correct to 2 decimal places.

- Be careful of extraneous solutions when solving equations involving logarithms and exponents. Make sure that you check your answers in the original equation.

Problems

1. Solve the following exponential equations.

    a. $4^x = 16$

    b. $\left(\dfrac{1}{8}\right)^x = 64$

2. Solve the following logarithmic equations.

    a. $\ln x = -7$

    b. $\ln(2x - 1) = 5$

3. Solve the following exponential equations. Round your result to 3 decimal places.

    a. $8^{3x} = 360$

    b. $\left(1 + \dfrac{0.10}{12}\right)^{12t} = 2$

    c. $e^{2x} - 4e^x - 5 = 0$

    d. $e^x = e^{x^2 - 2}$

4. Solve the following logarithmic equations. Round your result to 3 decimal places.

    a. $\log_5 (3x + 2) = \log_5 (6 - x)$

    b. $\log_4 x - \log_4 (x - 1) = \dfrac{1}{2}$

5. Use a graphing utility to approximate the solution of the equation $\log_{10} x = x^3 - 3$, accurate to 3 decimal places.

Exponential and Logarithmic Models

Lesson 11

Topics

- Exponential and logarithmic models.
- Exponential growth and decay.
- Gaussian models.
- Logistic growth models.
- Newton's law of cooling.

Models

- **Exponential growth model**: $y = ae^{bx}$, $b > 0$.

- **Exponential decay model**: $y = ae^{bx}$, $b < 0$.

- **Gaussian model**: $y = ae^{-(x-b)^2/c}$.

- **Logistic growth model**: $y = \dfrac{a}{1 + be^{-rx}}$.

- **Newton's law of cooling**: The rate of change in the temperature of an object is proportional to the difference between the object's temperature and the temperature of the surrounding medium.

Summary

In this lesson, we look at a variety of models involving exponential and logarithmic functions. Although these examples might seem fairly simple, they illustrate important ideas about mathematical modeling. The first model we consider is that of exponential growth.

Example 1: Modeling Exponential Growth

In a research experiment, a population of fruit flies is increasing according to the law of exponential growth. After 2 days there are 1000 flies, and after 4 days there are 3000 flies. According to this model, approximately how many flies will there be after 5 days?

Solution

Let y be the number of fruit flies at time t (in days). The model for exponential growth is $y = ae^{bt}$. We can determine the unknown constants by solving the following 2 equations.

$$t = 2 : y = 1000 = ae^{2b}$$
$$t = 4 : y = 3000 = ae^{4b}$$

From the first equation, you have $a = \dfrac{1000}{e^{2b}}$.

Substituting this value into the second equation, you obtain $3000 = ae^{4b} = \left(\dfrac{1000}{e^{2b}} \right) e^{4b} \Rightarrow 3 = e^{2b}$.

Using the inverse relationship between logarithms and exponents, we have $2b = \ln 3 \Rightarrow b = \dfrac{1}{2} \ln 3 \approx 0.5493$. Now we can find the value of the other constant:

$$a = \frac{1000}{e^{2b}} = \frac{1000}{e^{2\left[(\frac{1}{2}) \ln 3 \right]}} = \frac{1000}{3} \approx 333.33.$$

Hence, our model is approximately $y = ae^{bt} \approx 333.33 e^{0.5493t}$.

When $t = 5$, $y \approx 333.33 e^{0.5493(5)} \approx 5196$ fruit flies. Note that by letting $t = 0$ in the model, you see that the initial amount of flies is approximately 333.

Example 2: A Gaussian Model for SAT Scores

In 2005, the SAT math scores for college-bound seniors roughly followed the normal distribution $y = 0.0035 e^{-(x-520)^2 / 26,450}$, $200 \leq x \leq 800$. Graph this model and estimate the average SAT score x.

Solution

You can use a graphing utility to produce the bell-shaped curve in figure 11.1. The average score is the x-coordinate of the maximum value, $x = 520$.

Figure 11.1

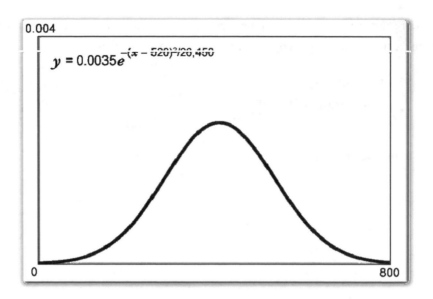

$$y = 0.0035e^{-(x - 520)^2/26,450}$$

Example 3: Newton's Law of Cooling

In this example, we analyze a specific application of Newton's law of cooling. Using calculus, it is possible to derive a mathematical model for Newton's law of cooling. Imagine a cup of coffee at $100°F$ placed in a room at $60°$. According to this law, the temperature of the coffee will decrease according to the equation $y = 60 + 40e^{-0.02877t}$, where t is the time in minutes. By evaluating this model for various values of t, you will see that the coffee is $90°$ after 10 minutes, and $82°$ 10 minutes later.

Study Tips

- For the exponential growth model, $b > 0$, whereas $b < 0$ for exponential decay. The constant a indicates the initial amount of the substance under consideration.
- The logistic growth model is used for populations that initially experience rapid growth, followed by a declining rate of growth. For example, a bacteria culture might grow rapidly at the beginning, but then increase more slowly as the amount of food and space diminishes.

Problems

1. Suppose you deposit $10,000 at 3.5% interest, compounded continuously. How long will it take for the deposit to double?

2. The half-life of Radium-226 is 1599 years. If there are 10 grams now, how much will there be after 1000 years?

3. The population P (in thousands) of Reno, Nevada, can be modeled by $P = 134.0e^{kt}$, where t is the year, with $t = 0$ corresponding to 1990. In 2000, the population was 180,000.

    a. Find the value of k for the model. Round your result to 4 decimal places.

    b. Use your model to predict the population in 2010.

4. The IQ scores for adults roughly follow the normal distribution $y = 0.0266e^{-(x-100)^2/450}$, $70 \le x \le 115$, where x is the IQ score.

    a. Use a graphing utility to graph the function.

    b. From the graph, estimate the average IQ score.

5. A conservation organization releases 100 animals of an endangered species into a game preserve. The organization believes that the preserve has a carrying capacity of 1000 animals and that the growth of the herd will follow the logistic curve

    $$p(t) = \frac{1000}{1 + 9e^{-0.1656t}},$$

    where t is measured in months.

    a. What is the population after 5 months?

    b. After how many months will the population reach 500?

    c. Use a graphing utility to graph the function. Use the graph to determine the values of p at which the horizontal asymptotes will occur. Interpret the meaning of the larger asymptote in the context of the problem.

Introduction to Trigonometry and Angles
Lesson 12

Topics

- Definition of angle.
- Coterminal angles.
- Complementary and supplementary angles.
- Degree measure and radian measure.
- Other units of angle measurement: minutes and seconds.
- Arc length formula.
- Linear and angular speed.

Definitions and Formulas

- An **angle** is determined by rotating a ray, or half-line, about its endpoint. The starting position of the ray is the initial side, and the end position is the terminal side. The endpoint of the ray is the **vertex**. If the origin is the vertex and the initial side is the positive x-axis, then the angle is in standard position.

- **Positive angles** are generated by a counterclockwise rotation, and **negative angles** by a clockwise rotation. If 2 angles have the same initial and terminal sides, then they are called **coterminal** angles.

- A measure of one **degree**, $1°$, is equivalent to a rotation of $1/360$ of a complete revolution about the vertex.

- An **acute angle** is between $0°$ and $90°$; a **right angle** is $90°$; an **obtuse angle** is between $90°$ and $180°$;

  a **straight angle** is $180°$. A **full revolution** is $360°$.

- Two positive angles are **complementary**, or complements of each other, if their sum is $90°$. Two positive angles are **supplementary**, or supplements of each other, if their sum is $180°$.

- Given a circle of radius 1, a **radian** is the measure of the central angle θ that intercepts (subtends) an arc s equal in length to the radius 1 of the circle.

- $180° = \pi$ radians, and 1 radian ≈ 57 degrees.

- One **minute** is $1/60$ of a degree. One **second** is $1/3600$ of a degree.

- Linear speed measures how fast a particle moves. **Linear speed** is arc length divided by time: $\dfrac{s}{t}$.

- Angular speed measures how fast the angle is changing. **Angular speed** is central angle divided by time: $\dfrac{\theta}{t}$.

- **Quadrant**: the 4 parts into which a plane is evenly divided by rectangular coordinate axes, see figure 12.1

Figure 12.1

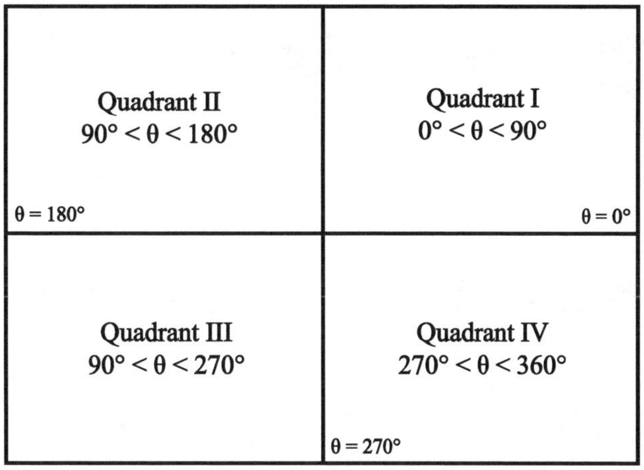

Quadrant II $90° < \theta < 180°$	Quadrant I $0° < \theta < 90°$
$\theta = 180°$	$\theta = 0°$
Quadrant III $90° < \theta < 270°$	Quadrant IV $270° < \theta < 360°$
	$\theta = 270°$

Summary

In this lesson, we begin the study of trigonometry. Before we define the trigonometric functions, we study angles and their measures. After some preliminary definitions, we define coterminal angles, those that have the same initial and terminal sides.

Example 1: Finding Coterminal Angles

Find 2 coterminal angles (one positive and one negative) for $\theta = -120°$.

Solution

You can add or subtract multiples of $360°$ to obtain coterminal angles, as follows.

$$-120° + 360° = 240°$$
$$-120° - 360° = -480°$$

Example 2: Converting Degrees to Radians

Radian measure is another way to measure angles. One radian is the measure of a central angle θ that intercepts an arc s equal in length to the radius of a unit circle (radius 1). That is, π radians equals $180°$. A radian is approximately $57°$.

$$90° = \left(90 \text{ deg}\right)\left(\frac{\pi \text{ rad}}{180 \text{ deg}}\right) = \frac{\pi}{2} \text{ radians}$$

Example 3: Converting Radians to Degrees

$$-\frac{7\pi}{6} \text{ rad} = \left(-\frac{7\pi}{6} \text{ rad}\right)\left(\frac{180 \text{ deg}}{\pi \text{ rad}}\right) = -210 \text{ degrees}$$

Example 4: Using the Formula $s = r\theta$

Consider a circle of radius r. Suppose the angle θ corresponds to the arc length s. That is, the angle θ subtends an arc of the circle of length s. Then we have the important formula $s = r\theta$. Find the length of the arc intercepted by a central angle of $240°$ in a circle with a radius of 4 inches.

Solution

First convert degrees to radians, then use the formula.

$$240° = \left(240 \text{ deg}\right)\left(\frac{\pi \text{ rad}}{180 \text{ deg}}\right) = \frac{4\pi}{3} \text{ radians}$$

$$s = r\theta = 4\left(\frac{4\pi}{3}\right) = \frac{16\pi}{3} \approx 16.76 \text{ inches}$$

Study Tips

- To convert degrees to radians, multiply by $\pi/180$.
- To convert radians to degrees, multiply by $180/\pi$.
- Notice in Examples 2 and 3 above how the units (degrees and radians) conveniently cancel.
- When no units for an angle are mentioned, assume that radian measure is implied.

Pitfalls

- Depending on the application, make sure your calculator is set in the correct mode: degree or radian.
- Angles greater than $90°$ do not have complements.

1. Determine the quadrant in which each angle lies.

    a. 150°

    b. 282°

    c. $\dfrac{\pi}{5}$

    d. $\dfrac{7\pi}{5}$

2. Sketch each angle in standard position.

    a. 30°

    b. −150°

    c. $\dfrac{3\pi}{4}$

    d. $\dfrac{5\pi}{6}$

3. Determine 2 coterminal angles in degree measure (one positive and one negative) for each angle. (Note: There are many correct answers.)

    a. $\theta = -495°$

    b. $\theta = 230°$

4. Determine 2 coterminal angles in radian measure (one positive and one negative) for each angle. (Note: There are many correct answers.)

    a. $\theta = -\dfrac{9\pi}{4}$

    b. $\theta = -\dfrac{2\pi}{15}$

5. Find (if possible) the complement and supplement of each angle.

    a. 24°

    b. 126°

    c. $\dfrac{\pi}{3}$

    d. $\dfrac{3\pi}{4}$

6. Rewrite each angle in radian measure as a multiple of π. Do not use a calculator.

    a. $30°$

    b. $150°$

7. Rewrite each angle in degree measure. Do not use a calculator.

    a. $\dfrac{3\pi}{2}$

    b. $-\dfrac{7\pi}{6}$

8. Find the radian measure of the central angle of a circle of radius 29 inches that intercepts an arc of length 8 inches.

9. Find the length of the arc on a circle of radius 2 meters intercepted by a central angle $\theta = 1$ radian.

10. Find the radius of a circle with an arc of length 36 feet and central angle $\theta = \dfrac{\pi}{2}$ radians.

11. Assuming that Earth is a sphere of radius 6378 kilometers, what is the difference in latitudes of Syracuse, New York, and Annapolis, Maryland, where Syracuse is 450 kilometers due north of Annapolis?

Trigonometric Functions—Right Triangle Definition
Lesson 13

Topics

- Pythagorean theorem.
- Triangle definition of the trigonometric functions.
- Trigonometric values for 30, 45, and 60 degrees.

Definitions and Properties

- Consider a right triangle with an acute angle θ. The 6 trigonometric functions are defined as follows.

$$\sin \theta = \frac{\text{opposite}}{\text{hypotenuse}} \qquad \csc \theta = \frac{\text{hypotenuse}}{\text{opposite}}$$

$$\cos \theta = \frac{\text{adjacent}}{\text{hypotenuse}} \qquad \sec \theta = \frac{\text{hypotenuse}}{\text{adjacent}}$$

$$\tan \theta = \frac{\text{opposite}}{\text{adjacent}} \qquad \cot \theta = \frac{\text{adjacent}}{\text{opposite}}$$

Theorem and Identities

- In any right triangle, the **Pythagorean theorem** is with sides a and b, and hypotenuse c, then $a^2 + b^2 = c^2$.

- Pythagorean identities are defined as follows.

  o $\sin^2 \theta + \cos^2 \theta = 1$

  o $\tan^2 \theta + 1 = \sec^2 \theta$

  o $1 + \cot^2 \theta = \csc^2 \theta$

- Reciprocal relationships found in trigonometry are as follows.

  o $\sec\theta = \dfrac{1}{\cos\theta}$

  o $\csc\theta = \dfrac{1}{\sin\theta}$

  o $\cot\theta = \dfrac{1}{\tan\theta}$

Summary

In this lesson, we develop the trigonometric functions using a right triangle definition. If you know the lengths of the 3 sides of a right triangle, then you can find the trigonometric functions of either acute angle.

Example 1: Calculating Trigonometric Functions

Calculate the 6 trigonometric functions for the right triangle in figure 13.1.

Figure 13.1

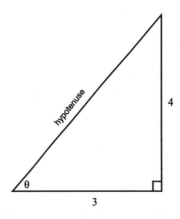

Solution

Using the Pythagorean theorem, the hypotenuse is 5: hypotenuse $= \sqrt{3^2 + 4^2} = \sqrt{25} = 5$.

$$\sin\theta = \frac{4}{5}, \quad \cos\theta = \frac{3}{5}, \quad \tan\theta = \frac{4}{3}$$
$$\csc\theta = \frac{5}{4}, \quad \sec\theta = \frac{5}{3}, \quad \cot\theta = \frac{3}{4}$$

Example 2: The 30-60-90 Right Triangle

Certain angles occur often in trigonometry. For example, the trigonometric values for 30 and 60 degrees are important to memorize.

Use the equilateral triangle in figure 13.2 to evaluate the sine and cosine of 30 and 60 degrees.

Figure 13.2

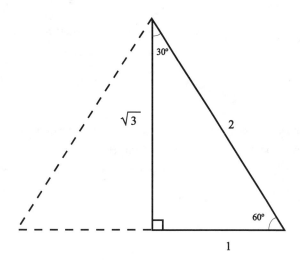

Solution

By drawing the altitude in the equilateral triangle, you have a 30-60-90 right triangle. If the hypotenuse is 2, then the shortest side is 1, and the third side is $\sqrt{3}$. The angle opposite the shortest side is $30°$. Hence, you have the following values.

$$\sin 30° = \sin \frac{\pi}{6} = \frac{1}{2} = \cos 60° = \cos \frac{\pi}{3}$$

$$\cos 30° = \cos \frac{\pi}{6} = \frac{\sqrt{3}}{2} = \sin 60° = \sin \frac{\pi}{3}$$

Observe in this example that cofunctions of complementary angles are equal. This is true in general.

Example 3: Finding Trigonometric Functions

The fundamental identities permit you to use a known value of one trigonometric function to determine the values of the other functions. Find the sine of the angle θ if you know that $\cos \theta = 0.8$.

Solution

We use the fundamental identity as follows.

$$\sin^2 \theta + \cos^2 \theta = 1$$
$$\sin^2 \theta + (0.8)^2 = 1$$
$$\sin^2 \theta = 1 - (0.8)^2 = 0.36$$
$$\sin \theta = 0.6$$

Knowing the sine and cosine, it is easy to determine the other 4 trigonometric functions.

Study Tips

- Notice that the tangent function could have been defined as the quotient of the sine and cosine.
- The power of a trigonometric function, such as $(\sin \theta)^2$ is written $\sin^2 \theta$.
- It is important to know the values of the trigonometric functions for common angles, such as $\frac{\pi}{6} = 30°$, $\frac{\pi}{4} = 45°$, $\frac{\pi}{3} = 60°$. Using an isosceles right triangle, for example, you can show that $\sin \frac{\pi}{4} = \cos \frac{\pi}{4} = \frac{\sqrt{2}}{2}$ and $\tan \frac{\pi}{4} = 1$.
- You can use a calculator to verify your answers. In fact, you *must* use a calculator to evaluate trigonometric functions for most angles.
- Cofunctions of complementary angles are equal. For example, $\tan 50° = \cot 40°$.
- On a calculator, you can evaluate the secant, cosecant, and cotangent as the reciprocal of cosine, sine, and tangent, respectively.
- The sine and cosine of any angle is less than or equal to one in absolute value.

Pitfall

- Make sure you have set your calculator in the correct mode: degree or radian. Not doing this is one of the most common mistakes in trigonometry.

1. Find the exact values of the 6 trigonometric functions of the angle θ shown in the following figures.

   a. Figure 13.3

$$b = \sqrt{13^2 - 5^2} = \sqrt{169 - 25} = 12$$

$$\sin \theta = \frac{\text{opp}}{\text{hyp}} = \frac{5}{13}$$

$$\cos \theta = \frac{\text{adj}}{\text{hyp}} = \frac{12}{13}$$

$$\tan \theta = \frac{\text{opp}}{\text{adj}} = \frac{5}{12}$$

$$\csc \theta = \frac{\text{hyp}}{\text{opp}} = \frac{13}{5}$$

$$\sec \theta = \frac{\text{hyp}}{\text{adj}} = \frac{13}{12}$$

$$\cot \theta = \frac{\text{adj}}{\text{opp}} = \frac{12}{5}$$

   b. Figure 13.4

$$C = \sqrt{18^2 + 12^2} = \sqrt{468} = 6\sqrt{13}$$

$$\sin \theta = \frac{18}{6\sqrt{13}} = \frac{3\sqrt{13}}{13}$$

$$\cos \theta = \frac{12}{6\sqrt{13}} = \frac{2\sqrt{13}}{13}$$

$$\tan \theta = \frac{18}{12} = \frac{3}{2}$$

$$\csc \theta = \frac{\sqrt{13}}{3}$$

$$\sec \theta = \frac{\sqrt{13}}{2}$$

$$\cot \theta = \frac{2}{3}$$

2. Sketch a right triangle corresponding to the trigonometric function of the acute angle θ given that $\sin\theta = \dfrac{2}{3}$. Use the Pythagorean theorem to determine the third side of the triangle, and then find the other 5 trigonometric functions of the angle.

3. Sketch a right triangle corresponding to the trigonometric function of the acute angle θ given that $\tan\theta = 3$. Use the Pythagorean theorem to determine the third side of the triangle, and then find the other 5 trigonometric functions of the angle.

4. Find the acute angle θ (in degrees and in radians) if $\cot\theta = \dfrac{\sqrt{3}}{3}$.

5. Find the acute angle θ (in degrees and in radians) if $\csc\theta = \sqrt{2}$.

6. Given the function values $\sin 60° = \dfrac{\sqrt{3}}{2}$ and $\cos 60° = \dfrac{1}{2}$, find the following trigonometric functions.

   a. $\tan 60°$

   b. $\sin 30°$

   c. $\cos 30°$

   d. $\cot 60°$

7. Given the function values $\csc\theta = 3$ and $\sec\theta = \dfrac{3\sqrt{2}}{4}$, find the following trigonometric functions.

   a. $\sin\theta$

   b. $\cos\theta$

   c. $\tan\theta$

   d. $\sec(90° - \theta)$

8. Use trigonometric identities to show that $(1 + \cos\theta)(1 - \cos\theta) = \sin^2\theta$.

9. Use a calculator to evaluate each function. Round your answers to 4 decimal places.

   a. $\sin 12°$

   b. $\cos 72°$

10. Without using a calculator, find the value of the acute angle θ (in degrees and radians) if $\sec\theta = 2$.

Trigonometric Functions—Arbitrary Angle Definition

Lesson 14

Topics

- Trigonometric functions for an arbitrary angle.
- Quadrants and the sign of trigonometric functions.
- Trigonometric values for common angles.
- Reference angles.
- Trigonometric functions as functions of real numbers.

Definitions

- Let θ be an angle in standard position, let (x, y) be a point on the terminal side, and let $r = \sqrt{x^2 + y^2} \neq 0$. The 6 trigonometric functions are defined as follows.

$$\sin \theta = \frac{y}{r} \quad \csc \theta = \frac{r}{y}$$

$$\cos \theta = \frac{x}{r} \quad \sec \theta = \frac{r}{x}$$

$$\tan \theta = \frac{y}{x} \quad \cot \theta = \frac{x}{y}$$

- Let θ be an angle in standard position. Its **reference angle** is the acute angle θ', formed by the terminal side of θ and the horizontal axis.

Quadrants and the Signs of the Trigonometric Functions

Quadrant II sin θ: + cos θ: − tan θ: −	Quadrant I sin θ: + cos θ: + tan θ: +
Quadrant III sin θ: − cos θ: − tan θ: +	Quadrant IV sin θ: − cos θ: + tan θ: −

Trigonometric Values of Common Angles

θ (degrees)	0°	30°	45°	60°	90°	180°	270°
θ (radians)	0	$\frac{\pi}{6}$	$\frac{\pi}{4}$	$\frac{\pi}{3}$	$\frac{\pi}{2}$	π	$\frac{3\pi}{3}$
$\sin\theta$	0	$\frac{1}{2}$	$\frac{\sqrt{2}}{2}$	$\frac{\sqrt{3}}{2}$	1	0	−1
$\cos\theta$	1	$\frac{\sqrt{3}}{2}$	$\frac{\sqrt{2}}{2}$	$\frac{1}{2}$	0	−1	0
$\tan\theta$	0	$\frac{\sqrt{3}}{3}$	1	$\sqrt{3}$	undef.	0	undef.

Summary

In this lesson, we define the trigonometric functions for an arbitrary angle. The definition is equivalent to the right triangle definition for acute angles. However, with this more general definition, we are able to calculate trigonometric values for any angle.

Example 1: Calculating Trigonometric Functions

Let $(-3, 4)$ be on the terminal side of the angle θ. Calculate the sine, cosine, and tangent of this angle.

Solution

We have $x = -3$, $y = 4$, and $r = \sqrt{(-3)^2 + 4^2} = \sqrt{25} = 5$. Then you have $\sin\theta = \dfrac{y}{r} = \dfrac{4}{5}$, $\cos\theta = \dfrac{x}{r} = -\dfrac{3}{5}$,

and $\tan\theta = \dfrac{y}{x} = -\dfrac{4}{3}$. Notice that the cosine and tangent are negative because the angle is in the Quadrant II.

Example 2: Important Angles

It is important to be familiar with the values of the trigonometric functions for frequently occurring angles. From the definitions of the sine, cosine, and tangent, you have the following.

$$\sin 0 = 0, \ \cos 0 = 1, \ \tan 0 = 0,$$

$$\sin\frac{\pi}{2} = 1, \ \cos\frac{\pi}{2} = 0, \ \tan\frac{\pi}{2} \text{ is undefined.}$$

Example 3: Using Reference Angles to Calculate Trigonometric Functions

Reference angles permit you to calculate trigonometric values for angles located in any quadrant. Calculate $\sin 300°$.

Solution

The reference angle for $300°$ is $60°$. Furthermore, $300°$ lies in Quadrant IV, so its sine is negative. Since $\sin 60° = \dfrac{\sqrt{3}}{2}$, we have $\sin 300° = -\dfrac{\sqrt{3}}{2}$.

We have defined the trigonometric functions for any angle—positive or negative. Hence, we can consider the trigonometric functions as functions of a real variable. Using x as the independent variable, you see that the domains of $f(x) = \sin x$ and $g(x) = \cos x$ are all real numbers, and their ranges consist of all real numbers in the interval $[-1, 1]$.

Study Tips

- For the definition of the 6 trigonometric functions, some authors specify that $r = 1$ in place of $r = \sqrt{x^2 + y^2}$. Both approaches yield the same values.

- Notice that some trigonometric functions are undefined for certain angles. For example, $\tan \frac{\pi}{2}$ is undefined because $\cos \frac{\pi}{2} = 0$.

- To find the value of a trigonometric function of an arbitrary angle θ:
  1. Determine the function value of the associated reference angle θ'.
  2. Depending on the quadrant, affix the appropriate plus or minus sign.

- You can use a calculator to verify your answer. For example, $\csc \frac{11\pi}{4} = \frac{1}{\sin \frac{11\pi}{4}} \approx 1.41421$, which approximates the exact answer $\frac{2}{\sqrt{2}} = \sqrt{2}$.

Pitfall

- Make sure you have set your calculator in the correct mode: degree or radian. This is one of the most common mistakes in trigonometry.

Problems

1. The point $(7, 24)$ is on the terminal side of an angle in standard position. Determine the exact values of the 6 trigonometric functions of the angle.

2. Find the values of the 6 trigonometric functions of the angle θ if $\sin \theta = \frac{3}{5}$ and θ lies in Quadrant II.

3. Find the values of the 6 trigonometric functions of the angle θ if $\csc \theta = 4$ and $\cot \theta < 0$.

4. Evaluate the following trigonometric functions.

    a. $\sec \pi$

b. $\tan \dfrac{\pi}{2}$

c. $\cot \pi$

d. $\csc \pi$

5. Find the reference angle θ' corresponding to the angle $\theta = 120°$. Sketch the 2 angles in standard position.

6. Evaluate the sine, cosine, and tangent of $\theta = 225°$ without using a calculator.

7. Evaluate the sine, cosine, and tangent of $\theta = -\dfrac{7\pi}{6}$ without using a calculator.

8. Use a calculator to evaluate $\sin 10°$. Round your answer to 4 decimal places.

9. Use a calculator to evaluate $\tan \dfrac{2\pi}{9}$. Round your answer to 4 decimal places.

10. The initial current and charge in an electric circuit are zero. When 100 volts is applied to the circuit, the current is given by $I = 5e^{-2t} \sin t$, where the resistance, inductance, and capacitance are 80 ohms, 20 henrys, and 0.01 farad, respectively. Approximate the current in amperes $t = 0.7$ seconds after the voltage is applied.

Graphs of Sine and Cosine Functions
Lesson 15

Topics

- Graphs of sine and cosine functions.
- Graphs of general sine and cosine functions: $y = d + a\sin(bx - c)$, $y = d + a\cos(bx - c)$.
- Amplitude.
- Period.
- Horizontal translations and phase shifts.
- Vertical translations.

Definitions

Given the general sine and cosine functions $y = d + a\sin(bx - c)$, $y = d + a\cos(bx - c)$, where $b > 0$,

- The **amplitude** is $|a|$. This number represents half the distance between the maximum and minimum values of the function.
- The **period** is $\dfrac{2\pi}{b}$ when angles are measured in radians.
- The **phase shift** is $\dfrac{c}{b}$.
- The constant d determines the **vertical translation.**

Summary

In this lesson, we study the graphs of sine and cosine functions. Recall that the domain of both $y = \sin x$ and $y = \cos x$ is the set of all real numbers, and the range consists of all real numbers in the closed interval $[-1, 1]$.

Example 1: The Graph of the Sine Function

To sketch the graph of $f(x) = \sin x$, begin calculating some values, such as $\sin 0 = 0$, $\sin\dfrac{\pi}{6} = \dfrac{1}{2}$, $\sin\dfrac{\pi}{4} = \dfrac{\sqrt{2}}{2}$, and $\sin\dfrac{\pi}{2} = 1$. Then connect these points with a smooth curve, as in figure 15.1.

Figure 15.1

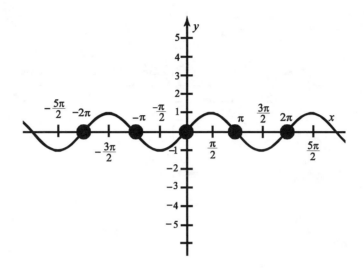

Notice that the sine function is odd (symmetric with respect to the origin). The x-intercepts are $0,\ \pm\pi,\ \pm 2\pi,\ \dots$. The maximum value of the sine function is 1, occurring at $x = \dfrac{\pi}{2},\ \dfrac{5\pi}{2},\ \dots,\ -\dfrac{3\pi}{2},\ -\dfrac{7\pi}{2},\ \dots$. The minimum value is -1, occurring at $x = \dfrac{3\pi}{2},\ \dfrac{7\pi}{2},\ \dots,\ -\dfrac{\pi}{2},\ -\dfrac{5\pi}{2},\ \dots$.

The graph of the cosine function is similar to that of the sine function. If you graph the cosine function on your calculator, you will see that it looks like the sine graph shifted to the left $\dfrac{\pi}{2}$ units.

Example 2: Periodicity

One of the most important properties of trigonometric functions is their periodicity. Sketch the graph of the function $f(x) = \sin\dfrac{x}{2}$.

Solution

The period is $\dfrac{2\pi}{b} = \dfrac{2\pi}{\frac{1}{2}} = 4\pi$. That means that the graph completes one cycle on the interval $\left[0,\ 4\pi\right]$. The x-intercepts are $x = 0,\ \pm 2\pi,\ \pm 4\pi,\ \dots$. Figure 15.2 shows both $y = \sin x$ and $f(x) = \sin\dfrac{x}{2}$.

Figure 15.2

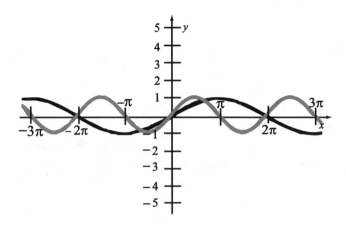

Example 3: Analyzing a Trigonometric Graph

This example analyzes a more complicated trigonometric graph, the function $y = \dfrac{1}{2}\sin\left(x - \dfrac{\pi}{3}\right)$.

Solution

The amplitude is $|a| = \left|\dfrac{1}{2}\right| = \dfrac{1}{2}$. The period is $\dfrac{2\pi}{b} = \dfrac{2\pi}{1} = 2\pi$. You can determine the left and right

endpoints of one cycle by solving the equations $x - \dfrac{\pi}{3} = 0$ and $x - \dfrac{\pi}{3} = 2\pi$. You will obtain $x = \dfrac{\pi}{3}$

and $x = \dfrac{7\pi}{3}$ as the endpoints of one complete cycle, as shown in figure 15.3. There is no vertical

shift $(d = 0)$.

Figure 15.3

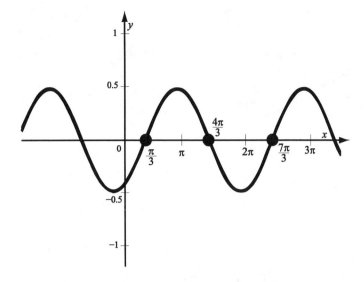

Study Tips

- The amplitude and vertical shift are generally easy to determine. For example, the graph of $y = 2 + 3\cos 2x$ is a vertical shift 2 units upward of the graph of $y = 3\cos 2x$.

- The **horizontal translations** are determined by solving the equations $bx - c = 0$ and $bx - c = 2\pi$.

- It is always a good idea to plot some points when analyzing a graph.

- You can also verify your graphs with a computer or graphing calculator.

Problems

1. Sketch the graph of the following functions by hand. Include 2 full periods.

   a. $y = 3\sin x$

   b. $y = \dfrac{1}{4}\cos x$.

   c. $y = \cos \dfrac{x}{2}$

   d. $y = \sin 4x$

e. $y = \sin\left(x - \dfrac{\pi}{4}\right)$

f. $y = \sin(x - \pi)$

2. Use a graphing utility to graph the following functions. Include 2 full periods. Identify the amplitude and period of the graphs.

a. $y = -2\sin\dfrac{2\pi x}{3}$

b. $y = -4 + 5\cos\dfrac{\pi t}{12}$

c. $y = 5\sin(\pi - 2x) + 10$

3. The pressure in millimeters of mercury, P, against the walls of the blood vessels of a person is modeled by $P = 100 - 20\cos\dfrac{8\pi t}{3}$, where t is the time in seconds. Use a graphing utility to graph the model, where one cycle is equivalent to one heartbeat. What is the person's pulse rate in heartbeats per minute?

Graphs of Other Trigonometric Functions

Lesson 16

Topics

- Graphs of other trigonometric functions.
- Graphs of general trigonometric functions.
- Damped trigonometric graphs.

Summary

In this lesson, we study graphs of the remaining 4 trigonometric functions. We begin with the graph of $y = \tan x$.

Example 1: The Graph of the Tangent Function

The function $f(x) = \tan x = \dfrac{\sin x}{\cos x}$ is not defined when $\cos x = 0$. The graph of the tangent function has vertical asymptotes at $x = \pm \dfrac{\pi}{2},\ \pm \dfrac{3\pi}{2},\ \pm \dfrac{5\pi}{2},\ \dots$ and intercepts at $x = 0,\ \pm \pi,\ \pm 2\pi,\ \dots$. If you plot some values and connect the points with smooth curves, you will obtain figure 16.1. Notice that the tangent is an odd function.

Figure 16.1

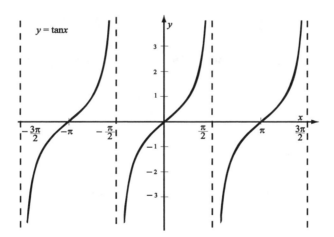

The period of the tangent function is π. The domain is the set of all real numbers except $x = \pm\dfrac{\pi}{2}, \ \pm\dfrac{3\pi}{2}, \ \pm\dfrac{5\pi}{2}, \ \dots$. The range is the set of all real numbers.

The graph of the cotangent function is similar to that of the tangent function, as shown in figure 16.2.

Figure 16.2

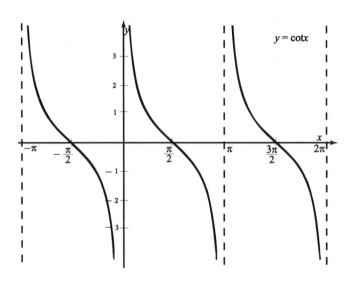

Example 2: The Graph of the Secant Function

Analyze the graph of $f(x) = \sec x = \dfrac{1}{\cos x}$, shown together with the cosine graph, as in figure 16.3. What are the period, x-intercepts, and vertical asymptotes.

Figure 16.3

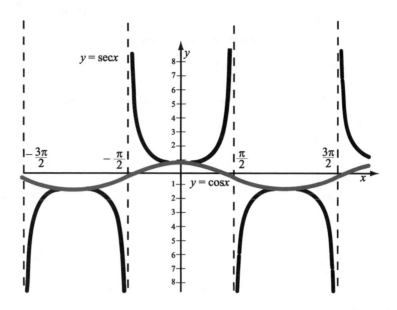

The period is 2π, and there are no x-intercepts. The graph has vertical asymptotes at $x = \pm\dfrac{\pi}{2},\ \pm\dfrac{3\pi}{2},\ \pm\dfrac{5\pi}{2},\ \dots$. The graph of the cosecant function is similar to that of the secant function.

Example 3: Analyzing a Damped Trigonometric Graph

In this example, we analyze a *damped* trigonometric graph. Analyze the graph of the function $f(x) = e^{-x}\sin x$.

Solution

Using a graphing utility, you will obtain the graph in figure 16.4.

Figure 16.4

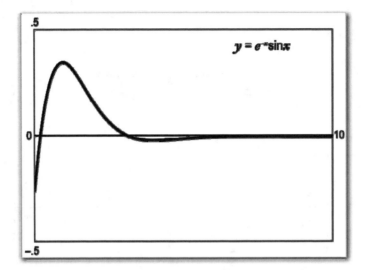

Notice that the graph approaches zero as x tends to infinity. This damping effect can be described in limit notation as $\lim\limits_{x \to \infty} e^{-x} \sin x = 0$.

Study Tips

- The vertical asymptotes of the tangent function, or secant function, are $x = \pm\dfrac{\pi}{2},\ \pm\dfrac{3\pi}{2},\ \pm\dfrac{5\pi}{2},\ \dots\,.$
  This can be written as $x = \dfrac{\pi}{2} + n\pi$, where n is an integer.

- You can obtain the graphs of cotangent, secant, and cosecant on a graphing utility by using $\cot x = \dfrac{1}{\tan x}$, $\sec x = \dfrac{1}{\cos x}$, and $\csc x = \dfrac{1}{\sin x}$.

- The function $f(x) = \sin\dfrac{1}{x}$ is fun to graph on your calculator. Zoom in on the graph near the origin and you will see some bizarre behavior.

Pitfall

- A graphing calculator might connect parts of the graphs of tangent, cotangent, secant, and cosecant that are not supposed to be connected. You can avoid this by using dot mode instead of connected mode.

1. Sketch the graph of the following functions by hand. Include 2 full periods

   a. $y = \dfrac{1}{2}\tan x$

   b. $y = \dfrac{1}{4}\sec x$

   c. $y = 3\csc\dfrac{x}{2}$

   d. $y = \dfrac{1}{2}\cot\dfrac{x}{2}$

2. Use a graphing utility to graph the following function, include 2 full periods: $y = 2\csc 3x$. Graph the corresponding reciprocal function, and compare the 2 graphs.

3. Use a graphing utility to graph the function, include 2 full periods: $y = -2\sec 4x$. Graph the corresponding reciprocal function, and compare the 2 graphs.

4. Use the graph of the function to approximate the solutions to the equation $\tan x = 1$ on the interval $\left[-2\pi,\ 2\pi\right]$.

5. Use a graphing utility to graph the 2 equations $y_1 = \sec^2 x - 1$ and $y_2 = \tan^2 x$ in the same viewing window. Use the graphs to determine whether the expressions are equivalent. Verify the result algebraically.

6. Use a graphing utility to graph the function $f(x) = e^{-x}\cos x$ and the damping factor of the function in the same viewing window. Describe the behavior of the function as x increases without bound.

7. An object weighing W pounds is suspended from a ceiling by a steel spring, see figure 16.5. The weight is pulled downward (positive direction) from its equilibrium position and released. The resulting motion of the weight is described by the function $y = \frac{1}{2}e^{-t/4}\cos 4t$, where y is the distance in feet, and t is the time in seconds $(t > 0)$.

    a. Use a graphing utility to graph the function.

    b. Describe the behavior of the displacement function for increasing values of time t.

63. ***Harmonic Motion*** An object weighing W pounds is suspended from a ceiling by a steel spring (see figure). The weight is pulled downward (positive direction) from its equilibrium position and released. The resulting motion of the weight is described by the function $y = \frac{1}{2}e^{-t/4}\cos 4t$, where y is the distance in feet and t is the time in seconds $(t > 0)$.

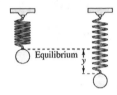

(a) Use a graphing utility to graph the function.

(b) Describe the behavior of the displacement function for increasing values of time t.

Inverse Trigonometric Functions

Lesson 17

Topics

- Inverse trigonometric functions.
- Graphs of inverse trigonometric functions.
- Inverse properties.

Properties

- $y = \arcsin x$ if and only if $\sin y = x$, $-1 \le x \le 1$, and $-\dfrac{\pi}{2} \le y \le \dfrac{\pi}{2}$.

- $y = \arccos x$ if and only if $\cos y = x$, $-1 \le x \le 1$, and $0 \le y \le \pi$.

- $y = \arctan x$ if and only if $\tan y = x$, $-\infty < x < \infty$, and $\dfrac{\pi}{2} < y < \dfrac{\pi}{2}$.

- $\sin(\arcsin x) = x$ and $\arcsin(\sin y) = y$ if $-1 \le x \le 1$, $-\dfrac{\pi}{2} \le y \le \dfrac{\pi}{2}$.

There are sSimilar properties for the other functions.

Summary

In this lesson, we study the inverse trigonometric functions. Because the 6 trigonometric functions are not one-to-one, we must restrict their domains in order to define their inverses. We begin with the inverse sine function.

Example 1: The Definition of the Inverse Sine Function

On the restricted interval $\left[-\dfrac{\pi}{2}, \dfrac{\pi}{2} \right]$, the sine function is one-to-one. We can define its inverse as follows:

$$y = \arcsin x = \sin^{-1} x \text{ if and only if } \sin y = x, \ -1 \le x \le 1, \text{ and} -\dfrac{\pi}{2} \le y \le \dfrac{\pi}{2}.$$

For example, $\arcsin \dfrac{1}{2} = \dfrac{\pi}{6}$ because $\sin \dfrac{\pi}{6} = \dfrac{1}{2}$ and $\dfrac{\pi}{6}$ lies in the interval $\left[-\dfrac{\pi}{2}, \dfrac{\pi}{2} \right]$.

The graph of the inverse sine function is a reflection in the line $y = x$ of the graph of the restricted sine function, see figure 17.1.

Figure 17.1

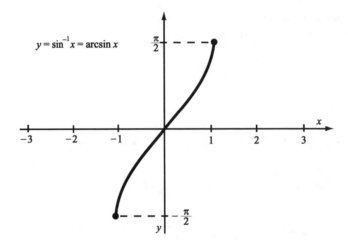

$$y = \sin^{-1} x = \arcsin x$$

Example 2: The Inverse Tangent Function

The remaining inverse trigonometric functions are defined in a similar manner by suitably restricting their domains. If we restrict the domain of the tangent function to the open interval $\left(-\dfrac{\pi}{2}, \dfrac{\pi}{2} \right)$, then it will be one-to-one, and we can define the inverse tangent function as follows:

$$y = \arctan x \text{ if and only if } \tan y = x, \ -\infty < x < \infty, \text{ and } -\frac{\pi}{2} < y < \frac{\pi}{2}.$$

For example, $\arctan(-1) = -\dfrac{\pi}{4}$ because $\tan\left(-\dfrac{\pi}{4} \right) = -1$ and $-\dfrac{\pi}{4}$ lies in the interval $\left(-\dfrac{\pi}{2}, \dfrac{\pi}{2} \right)$.

Notice that the graph of the arctangent function has 2 horizontal asymptotes: $y = \dfrac{\pi}{2}$ to the right and $y = -\dfrac{\pi}{2}$ to the left. See figure 17.2.

Figure 17.2

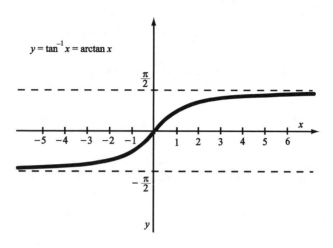

$$y = \sin\ x = \arcsin x$$

$$y = \tan^{-1} x = \arctan x$$

Example 3: Inverse Properties

We can take advantage of the properties of inverse functions, as long as we remember to verify the restricted domains.

$$\sin(\arcsin 1) = 1$$

$$\sin\left(\arcsin\frac{1}{5}\right) = \frac{1}{5}$$

$$\arcsin\left(\sin\frac{3\pi}{2}\right) = \arcsin(-1) = -\frac{\pi}{2}$$

Study Tips

- The key to defining the inverse trigonometric functions is to appropriately restrict the domains of the corresponding trigonometric functions.
- The 2 common notations for the inverse trigonometric functions are $y = \sin^{-1} x$ and $y = \arcsin x$ (and similarly for the other 5 inverse functions).
- Textbooks disagree on the definition of the inverse secant function. The difficulty is how to restrict the domain of the secant function so that it becomes one-to-one. Two popular choices are $\left[0, \frac{\pi}{2}\right) \cup \left(\frac{\pi}{2}, \pi\right]$ and $\left[0, \frac{\pi}{2}\right) \cup \left[\pi, \frac{3\pi}{2}\right)$.

Pitfalls

- Pay special attention to the restricted domains of the inverse trigonometric functions. For example, $\arccos(-1) \neq -\pi$ even though $\cos(-\pi) = -1$. In fact, $\arccos(-1) = \pi$.

- Similarly, $\arcsin(2)$ is undefined because there is no number x satisfying $\sin x = 2$.

- The notation for inverse trigonometric functions can be confusing. That is, $y = \sin^{-1} x$ does not mean $\dfrac{1}{\sin x}$.

Problems

1. Find the exact value of each expression without using a calculator.

   a. $\arccos \dfrac{1}{2}$

   b. $\arccos 0$

   c. $\arcsin 1$

   d. $\arccos 1$

   e. $\arctan 1$

   f. $\arctan 0$

   g. $\cos^{-1}\left(-\dfrac{\sqrt{2}}{2}\right)$

   h. $\sin^{-1}\left(-\dfrac{\sqrt{2}}{2}\right)$

2. Use a calculator to approximate the following values. Round your answer to the nearest hundredth.

   a. $\cos^{-1} 0.75$

   b. $\arcsin(-0.75)$

3. Use the properties of inverse functions to find the exact value of the following expressions

   a. $\sin(\arcsin 0.7)$

b. $\arcsin(\sin 3\pi)$

c. $\sin^{-1}\left(\tan \dfrac{5\pi}{4}\right)$

4. Find the exact value of the expression $\cos\left(\arcsin\left(\dfrac{24}{25}\right)\right)$.

5. Write an algebraic expression that is equivalent to $\cot(\arctan x)$.

Trigonometric Identities
Lesson 18

Topics

- Trigonometric identities.
- Graphs of inverse trigonometric functions.

Formulas and Identities

- Fundamental identities used to calculate trigonometric functions.

  o $\sin^2 u + \cos^2 u = 1$

  o $\tan^2 u + 1 = \sec^2 u$

  o $1 + \cot^2 u = \csc^2 u$

  o $\sin(-u) = -\sin u$

  o $\cos(-u) = \cos u$

  o $\tan(-u) = -\tan(u)$

- Confunction identities found in trigonometry are as follows.

  o $\sin\left(\dfrac{\pi}{2} - u\right) = \cos u$

  o $\cos\left(\dfrac{\pi}{2} - u\right) = \sin u$

  o $\tan\left(\dfrac{\pi}{2} - u\right) = \cot u$

- Reciprocal identities found in trigonometry are as follows.

  o $\sec u = \dfrac{1}{\cos u}$

  o $\csc u = \dfrac{1}{\sin u}$

     ○ $\cot u = \dfrac{1}{\tan u}$

Summary

In this lesson, we study trigonometric identities. In the first example, we use the fundamental identity $\sin^2 u + \cos^2 u = 1$ to calculate trigonometric functions.

Example 1: Using Identities to Evaluate Trigonometric Functions

Find the values of the trigonometric functions if $\sec u = -\dfrac{3}{2}$ and $\tan u > 0$.

Solution

We immediately know that $\cos u = \dfrac{1}{\sec u} = -\dfrac{2}{3}$. Furthermore, since cosine is negative and tangent is positive, angle u must be in Quadrant III. We can find the sine using the fundamental identity:

$$\sin^2 u = 1 - \cos^2 u = 1 - \left(-\dfrac{2}{3}\right)^2 = 1 - \dfrac{4}{9} = \dfrac{5}{9} \Rightarrow \sin u = -\dfrac{\sqrt{5}}{3}.$$

Notice that we take the negative square root since the angle is in Quadrant III. The remaining values are now simple to calculate:

$$\csc u = \dfrac{1}{\sin u} = -\dfrac{3}{\sqrt{5}} = -\dfrac{3\sqrt{5}}{5}, \quad \tan u = \dfrac{\sin u}{\cos u} = \dfrac{-\sqrt{5}/3}{-2/3} = \dfrac{\sqrt{5}}{2}, \text{ and } \cot u = \dfrac{1}{\tan u} = \dfrac{2}{\sqrt{5}} = \dfrac{2\sqrt{5}}{5}.$$

Example 2: Verifying a Trigonometric Identity

Verifying trigonometric identities is an important calculus topic. The secret is to begin with one side of the equation, and use your knowledge of trigonometric properties to arrive at the other side.

Verify the identity $\dfrac{\sec^2 \theta - 1}{\sec^2 \theta} = \sin^2 \theta.$

Solution

There are many ways to proceed. See if you can provide the reason for each step.

$$\frac{\sec^2 \theta - 1}{\sec^2 \theta} = \frac{\sec^2 \theta}{\sec^2 \theta} - \frac{1}{\sec^2 \theta}$$
$$= 1 - \cos^2 \theta$$
$$= \sin^2 \theta$$

Example 3: Verifying a Trigonometric Identity

Verify the identity $\tan^4 x = \tan^2 x \sec^2 x - \tan^2 x$.

Solution

We begin with the right-hand side, as follows.

$$\tan^2 x \sec^2 x - \tan^2 x = \tan^2 x \left(\sec^2 x - 1 \right) = \tan^2 x \left(\tan^2 x \right) = \tan^4 x$$

Study Tips

- In Example 1 above, we rationalized the denominator. Make sure to ask your teacher if this is necessary to do.
- A trigonometric equation is not an identity if it is false for at least one value in the domain. For example, $\sin x = \sqrt{1 - \cos^2 x}$ is not an identity because it is false for $x = \dfrac{3\pi}{2}$.
- Keep in mind the notation for powers of trigonometric functions. For example, $\sin^2 x$ means $\left(\sin x \right)^2$, not $\sin \left(x^2 \right) = \sin x^2$.
- You can confirm an identity by graphing both sides in the same viewing window. If the graphs look distinct, then the equation is not an identity. However, if the graphs appear to coincide, this is still not a valid proof.
- The sine and tangent functions are odd, so their graphs are symmetric about the origin. The cosine function is even, so its graph is symmetric about the y-axis.

Pitfalls

- Your answer to a problem might look different from another answer. For example, the expression $\ln |\sec \theta|$ is equivalent to $-\ln |\cos \theta|$ because $-\ln |\cos \theta| = \ln |\cos \theta|^{-1} = \ln |\sec \theta|$.

- When verifying a trigonometric identity, don't begin with the identity and simplify both sides simultaneously until you arrive at a true statement. This is not a proof technique. Here is an example of such a "false proof." The original statement is not true for all values of x.

$$\sin x = \sqrt{1 - \cos^2 x}$$
$$\sin^2 x = 1 - \cos^2 x$$
$$\sin^2 x + \cos^2 x = 1$$

Problems

1. Find the remaining trigonometric functions if $\sin x = \dfrac{1}{2}$ and $\cos x = \dfrac{\sqrt{3}}{2}$.

2. Find the remaining trigonometric functions if $\sin(-x) = -\dfrac{2}{3}$ and $\tan x = -\dfrac{2\sqrt{5}}{5}$.

3. Use the fundamental identities to simplify the following expressions.

   a. $\cot x \sin x$

   b. $\sec\alpha \dfrac{\sin\alpha}{\tan\alpha}$

4. Verify the following identities algebraically.

   a. $\dfrac{\cos\theta}{1 - \sin\theta} = \sec\theta + \tan\theta$

   b. $1 - \dfrac{\sin^2\theta}{1 - \cos\theta} = -\cos\theta$

5. Factor the following expression and use the fundamental identities to simplify: $\tan^4 x + 2\tan^2 x + 1$.

6. Simplify the expression $\dfrac{1}{1 + \cos x} + \dfrac{1}{1 - \cos x}$.

7. Verify the following identities.

   a. $\cos^2\beta - \sin^2\beta = 1 - 2\sin^2\beta.$

   b. $\dfrac{\tan x + \tan y}{1 - \tan x \tan y} = \dfrac{\cot x + \cot y}{\cot x \cot y - 1}.$

8. Use the properties of logarithms and trigonometric identities to verify the identity $\ln|\cot\theta| = \ln|\cos\theta| - \ln|\sin\theta|$.

Trigonometric Equations
Lesson 19

Topics

- Trigonometric equations.
- Approximate solutions to trigonometric equations.

Summary

In this lesson, we study trigonometric equations. Our goal is to identify all the values of the variable that satisfy the given equation. It is no exaggeration to say that this skill plays a major role in calculus. In our first example, notice how we first solve the equation on the interval $[0, 2\pi)$ and then use the periodicity of the sine function to obtain all solutions.

Example 1: Solving a Trigonometric Equation

Find all solutions to the equation $2\sin x - 1 = 0$.

Solution

The given equation is equivalent to $\sin x = \dfrac{1}{2}$. On the interval $[0, 2\pi)$, the solutions are $x = \dfrac{\pi}{6}$ and $x = \dfrac{5\pi}{6}$. By adding $2n\pi$ to each solution, where n is an integer, we obtain the complete set of solutions: $x = \dfrac{\pi}{6} + 2n\pi, \ x = \dfrac{5\pi}{6} + 2n\pi.$

Example 2: Solving a Trigonometric Equation

Find all solutions to the equation $2\sin^2 x - \sin x - 1 = 0$ on the interval $[0, 2\pi]$.

Solution

Begin by factoring the quadratic.

$$2\sin^2 x - \sin x - 1 = 0$$
$$(2\sin x + 1)(\sin x - 1) = 0$$

$$2\sin x + 1 = 0 \Rightarrow \sin x = -\frac{1}{2} \Rightarrow x = \frac{7\pi}{6}, \ \frac{11\pi}{6}$$

$$\sin x - 1 = 0 \Rightarrow \sin x = 1 \Rightarrow x = \frac{\pi}{2}$$

Thus, there are 3 solutions in the given interval: $x = \dfrac{7\pi}{6}, \ \dfrac{11\pi}{6}, \ \dfrac{\pi}{2}$. You are invited to verify these solutions by graphing $y = 2\sin^2 x - \sin x - 1$ and observing that the graph intersects the x-axis 3 times on the interval $[0, \ 2\pi]$.

Example 3: Approximating Solutions to a Trigonometric Equation

In many applications, it is impossible to find the exact solutions to a trigonometric equation. However, you can approximate the solutions with a computer or graphing utility. Use a graphing utility to approximate the solutions to the equation $x = 2\sin x$ on the interval $[-\pi, \ \pi]$.

Solution

Begin by graphing the function $y = x - 2\sin x$ on the given interval. You will see that there are 3 solutions to the equation. Using the root feature, you obtain $x \approx -1.8955$, $x = 0$, and $x = 1.8955$. Notice the symmetry of the solutions because the function is odd.

Study Tips

- In order to be successful in solving trigonometric equations, you have to know the values of common trigonometric functions. Many students memorize the values for important angles such as $\theta = 0$, $30°$, $45°$, $60°$, $90°$, and so on.
- You are encouraged to verify your solutions with a graphing utility. In fact, most graphing utilities have built-in root-finding capabilities.
- Some equations are easy to solve. For example, the fundamental identity $\sin^2 x + \cos^2 x = 1$ is valid for all x. Similarly, $\cos x = 2$ has no solutions because the range of the cosine function is $[-1, \ 1]$.

1. Find all solutions to the equation $\cos x = -\dfrac{1}{2}$ in the interval $[0°, \ 360°)$.

2. Find all solutions to the equation $\sin x = -\dfrac{\sqrt{2}}{2}$ in the interval $[0°, \ 360°)$.

3. Find all solutions to the equation $\cot x = -1$ in the interval $[0, \ 2\pi)$.

4. Find all solutions to the equation $\csc x = -2$ in the interval $[0, \ 2\pi)$.

5. Solve the equation $3\csc^2 x - 4 = 0$.

6. Find all solutions to the equation $\sec^2 x - \sec x = 2$ in the interval $[0, \ 2\pi)$ algebraically.

7. Find all solutions to the equation $2\sin x + \csc x = 0$ in the interval $[0, \ 2\pi)$ algebraically.

8. Use a graphing utility to approximate the solutions to the equation $2\sin^2 x + 3\sin x + 1 = 0$ in the interval $[0, \ 2\pi)$. Round your answer to 3 decimal places.

9. Use a graphing utility to approximate the solutions to the equation $3\tan^2 x + 5\tan x - 4 = 0$ in the interval $\left[-\dfrac{\pi}{2}, \ \dfrac{\pi}{2} \right]$. Round your answer to 3 decimal places.

10. Solve the multiple angle equation $\sin 4x = 1$.

11. Use a graphing utility to graph the function $f(x) = \cos\dfrac{1}{x}$.

    a. What is the domain of the function?

    b. Identify any symmetry or asymptotes of the graph.

    c. Describe the behavior of the function as $x \to 0$.

Sum and Difference Formulas
Lesson 20

Topics

- Sum and difference formulas.
- Double-angle formulas.
- Power reducing formulas.

Formulas

- Sum and difference formulas in trigonometry are as follows.

  o $\sin(u \pm v) = \sin u \cos v \pm \cos u \sin v \sin$

  o $\cos(u \pm v) = \cos u \cos v \mp \sin u \sin v$

  o $\tan(u \pm v) = \dfrac{\tan u \pm \tan v}{1 \mp \tan u \tan v}$

- Double-angle formulas in trigonometry are as follows.

  o $\sin 2u = 2 \sin u \cos u$

  o $\cos 2u = \cos^2 u - \sin^2 u = 2\cos^2 u - 1 = 1 - 2\sin^2 u$

- Power-reducing formulas in trigonometry are as follows.

  o $\sin^2 u = \dfrac{1 - \cos 2u}{2}$

  o $\cos^2 u = \dfrac{1 + \cos 2u}{2}$

Summary

In this lesson, we study the important formulas for the sum and difference of sines, cosines, and tangents. Unfortunately, the formulas are not as simple as we would like. For instance, in general, $\sin(u + v) \neq \sin u + \sin v$. We illustrate one of these new formulas in the first example.

Example 1: Evaluating a Trigonometric Function

Find the exact value of $\sin\dfrac{\pi}{12}$.

Solution

$\dfrac{\pi}{12}$ is not a common angle, but we can rewrite it as the difference between 2 common angles. The formula for the sine of the difference of 2 angles yields the final result.

$$\sin\frac{\pi}{12} = \sin\left(\frac{\pi}{3} - \frac{\pi}{4}\right)$$
$$= \sin\frac{\pi}{3}\cos\frac{\pi}{4} - \cos\frac{\pi}{3}\sin\frac{\pi}{4}$$
$$= \frac{\sqrt{3}}{2}\frac{\sqrt{2}}{2} - \frac{1}{2}\frac{\sqrt{2}}{2} = \frac{\sqrt{6}-\sqrt{2}}{4} \approx 0.258819$$

Example 2: Deriving a Double-Angle Formula

Double-angle formulas are derived from the sum and difference formulas. You can derive the formula for $\sin 2u$ by using the formula for the sine of a sum.

$$\sin 2u = \sin(u+u)$$
$$= \sin u \cos u + \cos u \sin u$$
$$= 2\sin u \cos u$$

A similar argument and the fundamental identity yield the 3 formulas for $\cos 2u$. These formulas are given in the Theorems and Formula appendix.

Example 3: Solving a Trigonometric Equation

Double-angle formulas permit us to solve more complicated trigonometric equations. Solve the equation $2\cos x + \sin 2x = 0$ on the interval $[0,\ 2\pi]$.

Solution

We use the double-angle formula for the sine function, and then factor.

$$2\cos x + \sin 2x = 0$$
$$2\cos x + 2\sin x \cos x = 0$$
$$2\cos x(1+\sin x) = 0$$

$$\cos x = 0 \Rightarrow x = \frac{\pi}{2}, \ \frac{3\pi}{2}$$
$$\sin x = -1 \Rightarrow x = \frac{3\pi}{2}$$

Thus there are 2 solutions on the interval, $x = \dfrac{\pi}{2}$ and $x = \dfrac{3\pi}{2}$. Try verifying this result by graphing the function $y = 2\cos x + \sin 2x$ on the interval $[0, \ 2\pi]$.

Study Tips

- A computer or graphing calculator might give a different form of a correct answer. For instance, in Example 1, my calculator gave $\dfrac{\left(\sqrt{3}-1\right)\sqrt{2}}{4}$, which is also correct.

- The symbol $\pm$ and $\mp$ are used to conveniently combine formulas. For example, the formula $\cos(u \pm v) = \cos u \cos v \mp \sin u \sin v$ is shorthand for the 2 formulas $\cos(u+v) = \cos u \cos v - \sin u \sin v$ and $\cos(u-v) = \cos u \cos v + \sin u \sin v$.

- There are many more formulas in trigonometry. Please see the Theorem and Formula appendix for a list of the most important ones.

Pitfall

- You have to be careful with notation. There is a difference between the sine of the angle h, $\sin h = \sin(h)$, and the so-called hyperbolic function $\sinh$. This latter is a function used in engineering and is defined $\sinh x = \dfrac{e^x - e^{-x}}{2}$.

1. Find the exact value of each expression.

   a. $\cos(240° - 0°)$

   b. $\cos 240° - 0°$

   c. $\sin\left(\dfrac{2\pi}{3} + \dfrac{5\pi}{6}\right)$

   d. $\sin\dfrac{2\pi}{3} + \sin\dfrac{5\pi}{6}$

2. Find the exact values of the sine, cosine, and tangent of the angle $75°$.

3. Find the exact values of the sine, cosine, and tangent of the angle $\dfrac{13\pi}{12}$.

4. Write the expression $\cos 60° \cos 20° - \sin 60° \sin 20°$ as the sine, cosine, or tangent of an angle.

5. Write the expression $\cos\dfrac{\pi}{9}\cos\dfrac{\pi}{7} - \sin\dfrac{\pi}{9}\sin\dfrac{\pi}{7}$ as the sine, cosine, or tangent of an angle.

6. Find the exact value of $\tan(u + v)$ given that $\sin u = \dfrac{5}{13}$ and $\cos v = -\dfrac{3}{5}$. Both u and v are in Quadrant II.

7. Find the exact value of the expression $\sin\left(\sin^{-1}1 + \cos^{-1}1\right)$ without using a calculator.

8. Verify the identity $\sin(x + y) + \sin(x - y) = 2\sin x \cos y$.

9. Use a double-angle formula to rewrite the expression $8\sin x \cos x$.

10. Rewrite the expression $\sin^2 2x$ in terms of the first power of the cosine.

Law of Sines

Lesson 21

Topics

- The law of sines.
- Angle-angle-side (AAS) and angle-side-angle (ASA) problems.
- Side-side-angle (SSA) problems.
- Area formula.

Definitions

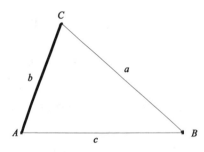

- Given the image above, the **law of sines** is defined as $\dfrac{a}{\sin A} = \dfrac{b}{\sin B} = \dfrac{c}{\sin C}$

- Given the image above, the **area formula** is defined as $\text{Area} = \dfrac{1}{2}bc\sin A = \dfrac{1}{2}ac\sin B = \dfrac{1}{2}ab\sin C$.

Summary

In this lesson and the next, we use trigonometry to "solve triangles." That is, given some sides and angles of a triangle, we will use the law of sines in this lesson, and the law of cosines in the next lesson, to determine the remaining sides and angles. The law of sines is used when you know 2 angles and a side, or 2 sides and one opposite angle. The law of cosines is used when you know 2 sides and the included angle, or all 3 sides. We illustrate an application of the law of sines in our first example.

Example 1: Using the Law of Sines

Given the triangle in figure 21.1, find the remaining sides and angle.

Figure 21.1

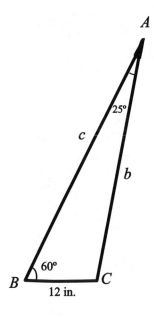

Solution

The third angle is easy to determine: $C = 180° - A - B = 180° - 25° - 60° = 95°$. We use the law of sines to calculate the remaining 2 sides. Note that we need to use our calculator set in degree mode.

$$\frac{b}{\sin B} = \frac{a}{\sin A} \Rightarrow b = \frac{a}{\sin A}(\sin B) = \frac{12}{\sin 25°}(\sin 60°) \approx 24.59 \text{ in.}$$

$$\frac{c}{\sin C} = \frac{a}{\sin A} \Rightarrow c = \frac{a}{\sin A}(\sin C) = \frac{12}{\sin 25°}(\sin 95°) \approx 28.29 \text{ in.}$$

Example 2: The 2-Solution Case

Two angles and one side determine a unique triangle (AAS or ASA). However, the situation is more complicated if you are given 2 sides and one opposite angle. In this case, there might be exactly one triangle, no triangle, or 2 different triangles. This example illustrates the 2-triangle case. Solve the triangle if you are given $a = 2$, $b = \sqrt{12}$, and $A = 30°$.

Solution

The law of sines gives $\dfrac{\sin B}{b} = \dfrac{\sin A}{a} \Rightarrow \sin B = \dfrac{\sin A}{a}(b) = \dfrac{\sin 30°}{2}\left(\sqrt{12}\right) = \dfrac{\frac{1}{2}}{2}(2\sqrt{3}) = \dfrac{\sqrt{3}}{2}$.

There are 2 angles whose sine equals $\dfrac{\sqrt{3}}{2}$, $B = 60°$ and $B = 120°$. In the first case, $C = 180° - 30° - 60° = 90°$.

The triangle is a 30-60-90 right triangle and the hypotenuse is $c = \sqrt{2^2 + \left(\sqrt{12}\right)^2} = \sqrt{4 + 12} = 4$. For the second case, $C = 180° - 30° - 120° = 30°$. The triangle is isosceles and the third side is 2.

Example 3: An Area Application

The law of sines can be used to develop a convenient formula for the area of any triangle. Find the area of the triangular lot having 2 sides of lengths 90 meters and 52 meters and an included angle of 102°.

Solution

Since we are given 2 sides and the included angle, we can use the area formula to find the following.

$$A = \frac{1}{2}ab\sin C = \frac{1}{2}(90)(52)\sin 102° \approx 2288.87 \text{ m}^2.$$

Study Tips

- The law of sines is often presented in the equivalent form $\dfrac{\sin A}{a} = \dfrac{\sin B}{b} = \dfrac{\sin C}{c}$.
- The side-side-angle case is the most difficult. As Example 2 above shows, it is possible to have 2 distinct solutions. It is also possible to have exactly one solution or no solution at all.
- It is always helpful to draw a sketch when solving triangles.

Problems

1. Use the law of sines to solve the triangle if $A = 36°$, $a = 8$, and $b = 5$.

2. Use the law of sines to solve the triangle if $A = 60°$, $a = 9$, and $c = 10$.

3. Use the law of sines to solve the triangle if $A = 102.4°$, $C = 16.7°$, and $a = 21.6$.

4. Use the law of sines to solve the triangle if $A = 76°$, $a = 18$, and $b = 20$.

5. Use the law of sines to solve the triangle if $A = 58°$, $a = 4.5$, and $b = 12.8$.

6. Find the area of the triangle if $C = 110°$, $a = 6$, and $b = 10$.

7. Find the area of the triangle if $C = 38°45'$, $b = 67$, and $c = 85$.

8. The circular arc of a railroad curve has a chord of length 3000 feet and a central angle of $40°$. Find the radius and length of the circular arc.

(a)

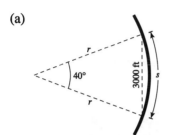

(b) $r = \dfrac{3000 \sin[1/2(180° - 40°)]}{\sin 40°} \approx 4385.71$ feet

(c) $s \approx 40°\left(\dfrac{\pi}{180°}\right)4385.71 \approx 3061.80$ feet

Law of Cosines
Lesson 22

Topics

- The law of cosines.
- Side-side-side (SSS) and side-angle-side (SAS) problems.
- Side-side-angle (SSA) problems.
- Heron's area formula.

Definitions

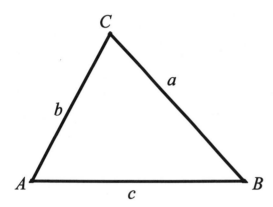

- Given the image above, the **law of cosines** is defined as follows.

    o $a^2 = b^2 + c^2 - 2bc \cos A$

    o $\mathbf{s}\, b^2 = a^2 + c^2 - 2ac \cos B$

    o $c^2 = a^2 + b^2 - 2ab \cos C$

- Given a triangle with sides a, b, and c, Heron's area formula states the area $= \sqrt{s(s-a)(s-b)(s-c)}$, where $s = \dfrac{a+b+c}{2}$.

Summary

This is our second lesson on "solving triangles." Here we use the law of cosines, a generalization of the Pythagorean theorem, to determine the remaining sides and angles in the cases side-side-side (SSS) and side-angle-side (SAS). Our first example illustrates the case side-side-side.

Example 1: Using the Law of Cosines for the Case SSS

Given the triangle in figure 22.1, find the 3 angles.

Figure 22.1

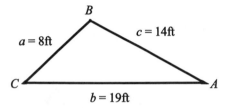

Solution

We begin by using the law of cosines to calculate the angle opposite the longest side.

$$b^2 = a^2 + c^2 - 2ac\cos B$$

$$\cos B = \frac{a^2 + c^2 - b^2}{2ac} = \frac{8^2 + 14^2 - 19^2}{2(8)(14)} \approx -0.45089$$

Using a calculator, you obtain $B \approx 116.80°$. Notice that the angle is obtuse because its cosine is negative. For the second angle, you can use the law of cosines again or the law of sines. Using the latter, we obtain the following.

$$\frac{\sin A}{a} = \frac{\sin B}{b} \Rightarrow \sin A = a\left(\frac{\sin B}{b}\right) \approx 8\left(\frac{\sin 116.80°}{19}\right) \approx 0.37583$$

$$A \approx 22.08°$$

Finally, $C = 180° - A - B = 180° - 22.08° - 116.80° = 41.12°$.

Example 2: Using the Law of Cosines for the Case SAS

This example considers the case side-angle-side. Solve the triangle in figure 22.2.

Figure 22.2

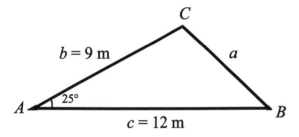

Solution

Using the law of cosines, $a^2 = b^2 + c^2 - 2bc \cos A = 9^2 + 12^2 - 2(9)(12) \cos 25° \approx 29.2375$, $a \approx \sqrt{29.2375} \approx 5.4072$

Now use the law of sines to find the angle B: $\dfrac{\sin B}{b} = \dfrac{\sin A}{a} \Rightarrow \sin B = b\left(\dfrac{\sin A}{a}\right) \approx 9\left(\dfrac{\sin 25°}{5.4072}\right) \approx 0.7034$. Because c is the longest side, the angle B must be acute, and you can use a calculator to obtain $B \approx 44.7°$.

Finally, $C = 180° - 44.7° - 25° = 110.3°$.

Example 3: An Area Application

The law of cosines can be used to develop another convenient formula for the area of a triangle. Use Heron's formula to find the area of a 3-4-5 right triangle.

Solution

The semiperimeter is $s = \dfrac{a+b+c}{2} = \dfrac{3+4+5}{2} = 6$. Hence, Heron's formula gives

$A = \sqrt{s(s-a)(s-b)(s-c)} = \sqrt{6(6-3)(6-4)(6-5)} = \sqrt{36} = 6.$

Study Tips

- The law of cosines can be written many ways. For example, $\cos A = \dfrac{b^2 + c^2 - a^2}{2bc}$.
- If a triangle is a right triangle, $\cos 90° = 0$, the law of cosines simplifies to the Pythagorean theorem.
- In the first example, we found the largest angle first. If this angle is obtuse, then the other 2 angles are acute. And if this angle is acute, then so are the others. Recall that $\cos\theta > 0 \Rightarrow$ angle acute and $\cos\theta < 0 \Rightarrow$ angle obtuse.

Pitfalls

- You cannot apply the law of cosines to any 3 lengths a, b, and c. For example, if $a = 16$, $b = 4$, and $c = 10$, you would obtain $\cos A = \dfrac{b^2 + c^2 - a^2}{2bc} = -1.75$, which is impossible. In fact, these 3 lengths cannot form a triangle because $16 > 4 + 10$.

- Similarly, Heron's area formula would not work for these 3 lengths because you would obtain the square root of a negative number.

Problems

1. Use the law of cosines to solve the triangle if $a = 6$, $b = 8$, and $c = 12$.

2. Use the law of cosines to solve the triangle if $a = 50°$, $b = 15$, and $c = 30$.

3. Use the law of cosines to solve the triangle if $a = 9$, $b = 12$, and $c = 15$.

4. Use Heron's area formula to find the area of the triangle if $a = 5$, $b = 8$, and $c = 10$.

5. Use Heron's area formula to find the area of the triangle if $a = 3.5$, $b = 10.2$, and $c = 9$.

6. Two ships leave a port at 9 a.m. One travels at a bearing of N 53° W at 12 miles per hour, and the other travels at a bearing of S 67° W at 16 miles per hour. Approximate how far apart the ships are at noon that day.

Introduction to Vectors
Lesson 23

Topics

- Vectors.
- Vector operations.
- Unit vectors.

Definitions and Formulas

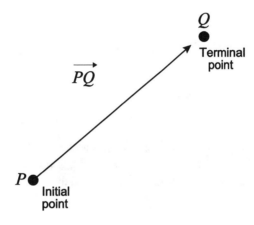

- Given a **directed line segment** $\overrightarrow{PQ}$, P is the **initial point**, and Q is the **terminal point**.

- The length or **magnitude** of a directed line segment is denoted $\left\| \overrightarrow{PQ} \right\|$.

- Directed line segments having the same length and direction are called **equivalent**. The set of all directed line segments that are equivalent to a given $\overrightarrow{PQ}$ is a **vector** in the plane, $\mathbf{v} = \overrightarrow{PQ}$.

- If the initial point of a directed line segment is at the origin, then the vector is in **standard position**. It is uniquely represented by the coordinates $(v_1,\, v_2)$ of its terminal point: $\mathbf{v} = \langle v_1,\, v_2 \rangle$. These coordinates are the **components** of the vector.

- The **component form** of a vector with initial point $P = (p_1,\, p_2)$ and terminal point $Q = (q_1,\, q_2)$ is
  $$\overrightarrow{PQ} = \langle q_1 - p_1,\, q_2 - p_2 \rangle = \langle v_1,\, v_2 \rangle = \mathbf{v}.$$

- $\|\mathbf{v}\| = \sqrt{v_1^2 + v_2^2}$. The vector $\mathbf{v}$ is a unit vector if $\|\mathbf{v}\| = 1$.

- The standard **unit vectors** are $\mathbf{i} = \langle 1,\ 0 \rangle$ and $\mathbf{j} = \langle 0,\ 1 \rangle$.

- The **trigonometric form** of a vector is $\mathbf{v} = \|\mathbf{v}\|(\cos\theta\,\mathbf{i} + \sin\theta\,\mathbf{j})$. Here, the direction angle θ is the angle the vector makes with the positive x-axis.

- The term **scalar** is just another word for a real number.

Vector Operations

Let $\mathbf{u} = \langle u_1,\ u_2 \rangle$, $\mathbf{v} = \langle v_1,\ v_2 \rangle$, and let k be a real number.

- Addition: $\mathbf{u} + \mathbf{v} = \langle u_1 + v_1,\ u_2 + v_2 \rangle$.

- Scalar multiplication: $k\mathbf{u} = k\langle u_1,\ u_2 \rangle = \langle ku_1,\ ku_2 \rangle$.

Summary

In this lesson, vectors are used to represent quantities that have both magnitude and direction (e.g., velocity, acceleration, force). We use directed line segments joining 2 points to represent vectors. Two directed line segments are equivalent if they have the same magnitude and direction, as illustrated in the first example.

Example 1: Equivalent Directed Line Segments

Let $\mathbf{u}$ be represented by the directed line segment from $P = (0,\ 0)$ to $Q = (3,\ 2)$, and let $\mathbf{v}$ be represented by the directed line from $R = (1,\ 2)$ to $S = (4,\ 4)$. Show that $\mathbf{u} = \mathbf{v}$.

Solution

We begin by using the distance formula to show that the magnitudes are equal.

$$\left\|\overrightarrow{PQ}\right\| = \sqrt{(3-0)^2 + (2-0)^2} = \sqrt{9+4} = \sqrt{13}$$
$$\left\|\overrightarrow{RS}\right\| = \sqrt{(4-1)^2 + (4-2)^2} = \sqrt{9+4} = \sqrt{13}$$

We verify that the directions are the same by calculating the slopes of each line segment.

$$\text{slope of } \overrightarrow{PQ} = \frac{2-0}{3-0} = \frac{2}{3}$$

$$\text{slope of } \overrightarrow{RS} = \frac{4-2}{4-1} = \frac{2}{3}$$

The directed line segments have the same length and direction, which verifies that $\mathbf{u} = \mathbf{v}$.

Example 2: Vector Operations

You can add vectors and multiply them by real numbers. Find $\mathbf{v} + 2\mathbf{w}$ if $\mathbf{v} = \langle -2,\ 5 \rangle$ and $\mathbf{w} = \langle 3,\ 4 \rangle$.

Solution

$$2\mathbf{w} = 2\langle 3,\ 4 \rangle = \langle 6,\ 8 \rangle \Rightarrow \mathbf{v} + 2\mathbf{w} = \langle -2,\ 5 \rangle + \langle 6,\ 8 \rangle = \langle 4,\ 13 \rangle$$

Example 3: The Trigonometric Form of a Vector

We can combine our knowledge of trigonometry to express vectors in trigonometric form. Express the vector $\mathbf{v} = \langle 3,\ 3 \rangle$ in trigonometric form.

Solution

The magnitude of the vector is $\|\mathbf{v}\| = \sqrt{3^2 + 3^2} = \sqrt{18} = 3\sqrt{2}$. The vector makes an angle of $45°$ with the positive x-axis. Hence, the trigonometric form is the following.

$$\mathbf{v} = \|\mathbf{v}\|\left(\cos\theta\,\mathbf{i} + \sin\theta\,\mathbf{j}\right) = 3\sqrt{2}\left(\cos 45°\,\mathbf{i} + \sin 45°\,\mathbf{j}\right)$$

Study Tips

- The notation for vectors varies in science and engineering, as does the notation for magnitude. This can be confusing, so make sure to check your textbook.
- A vector $\mathbf{v}$ is the zero vector $\langle 0,\ 0 \rangle$ if and only if $\|\mathbf{v}\| = 0$.
- In this course, we consider vectors in the plane. In engineering and science, you also study vectors in space (3 dimensions).
- Scalar multiplication by a negative number reverses the direction of a nonzero vector.
- Given a nonzero vector $\mathbf{v}$, the vector $\dfrac{\mathbf{v}}{\|\mathbf{v}\|}$ is a unit vector in the same direction as $\mathbf{v}$.

Pitfalls

- Do not confuse the standard unit vector **i** with the imaginary number $i = \sqrt{-1}$.

- The magnitude of a sum of 2 vectors is not generally equal to the sum of their magnitudes. For example, $\|\mathbf{i}\| = \|\mathbf{j}\| = 1$ but $\|\mathbf{i} + \mathbf{j}\| = \|\langle 1,1 \rangle\| = \sqrt{2}$.

Problems

1. Find the component form and magnitude of the vector with initial point $\left(\dfrac{2}{5}, 1 \right)$ and terminal point $\left(1, \dfrac{2}{5} \right)$.

2. Find the component form and magnitude of the vector with initial point $\left(-\dfrac{2}{3}, -1 \right)$ and terminal point $\left(\dfrac{1}{2}, \dfrac{4}{5} \right)$.

3. Find $2\mathbf{u} - 3\mathbf{v}$ if $\mathbf{u} = \langle 4, 2 \rangle$ and $\mathbf{v} = \langle 7, 1 \rangle$.

4. Find a unit vector in the direction of the vector $\langle 6, 0 \rangle$.

5. Find a unit vector in the direction of the vector $\langle -24, -7 \rangle$.

6. Find the vector **v** having magnitude 8 and direction $\mathbf{u} = -2\mathbf{i}$.

7. The initial point of a vector is $(-3, 1)$, and the terminal point is $(4, 5)$. Write this vector as a linear combination of the unit vectors **i** and **j**.

8. Find the magnitude and direction angle of the vector $\mathbf{v} = 6\mathbf{i} - 6\mathbf{j}$.

9. Find the component form of the vector **v** if $\|\mathbf{v}\| = 3\sqrt{2}$ and **v** makes an angle of $\theta = 150°$ with the positive x-axis.

10. Find the component form of the vector that represents the velocity of an airplane descending at a speed of 100 miles per hour at an angle of $30°$ below the horizontal.

Lesson 23: Introduction to Vectors

108

Trigonometric Form of a Complex Number

Lesson 24

Topics

- The trigonometric form of a complex number.
- Multiplication and division using the trigonometric form.
- DeMoivre's theorem.

Definitions and Theorem

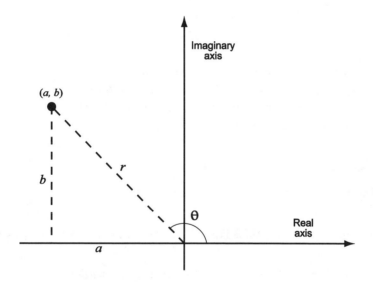

- The **absolute value** or **modulus** of a complex number $a+bi$ is $|a+bi| = \sqrt{a^2+b^2}$.

- The **trigonometric form** of the complex number $z = a+bi$ is $z = r(\cos\theta + i\sin\theta)$, where r is the absolute value and θ is the appropriate angle given by $\tan\theta = \dfrac{b}{a}$.

- Let $z_1 = r_1\left(\cos\theta_1 + i\sin\theta_1\right)$, and $z_2 = r_2\left(\cos\theta_2 + i\sin\theta_2\right)$. Multiplication and division using trigonometric form is defined as follows.

  o Multiplication: $z_1 z_2 = r_1 r_2 \left[\cos\left(\theta_1 + \theta_2\right) + i\sin\left(\theta_1 + \theta_2\right)\right].$

  o Division: $\dfrac{z_1}{z_2} = \dfrac{r_1}{r_2}\left[\cos\left(\theta_1 - \theta_2\right) + i\sin\left(\theta_1 - \theta_2\right)\right],\ z_2 \neq 0.$

- **DeMoivre's Theorem** is defined as follows: If $z = r\left(\cos\theta + i\sin\theta\right)$ and n is a positive integer, then $z^n = r^n\left(\cos n\theta + i\sin n\theta\right).$

- For a positive integer n, the complex number $z = r\left(\cos\theta + i\sin\theta\right)$ has exactly n distinct n^{th} roots given by $\sqrt[n]{r}\left(\cos\dfrac{\theta + 2\pi k}{n} + i\sin\dfrac{\theta + 2\pi k}{n}\right),\ k = 0,\ 1,\ \dots,\ n-1.$

Summary

In this lesson, we apply our trigonometric skills to complex numbers. We will see how to represent complex numbers in a new way and how to conveniently multiply and divide them. Finally, we will study the famous DeMoivre's theorem concerning powers and roots of complex numbers. We begin by showing how to find the trigonometric form of a complex number.

Example 1: The Trigonometric Form of a Complex Number

If $z = -2 - 2\sqrt{3}i$, then its absolute value is $r = \left|-2 - 2\sqrt{3}i\right| = \sqrt{\left(-2\right)^2 + \left(-2\sqrt{3}\right)^2} = \sqrt{4 + 12} = 4$. If you graph this complex number, you will see that it lies in the Quadrant III and $\tan\theta = \dfrac{b}{a} = \dfrac{-2\sqrt{3}}{-2} = \sqrt{3} \Rightarrow \theta = \dfrac{4\pi}{3}$. Hence, the trigonometric form is $z = r\left(\cos\theta + i\sin\theta\right) = 4\left(\cos\dfrac{4\pi}{3} + i\sin\dfrac{4\pi}{3}\right)$. You can easily check this answer by converting back to the original Cartesian coordinates.

Example 2: Multiplication

To multiply 2 complex numbers in trigonometric form, add their angles and multiply their absolute values. Find the product of the complex numbers $z_1 = -1 + \sqrt{3}i = 2\left(\cos\dfrac{2\pi}{3} + i\sin\dfrac{2\pi}{3}\right)$ and $z_2 = 4\sqrt{3} - 4i = 8\left(\cos\dfrac{11\pi}{6} + i\sin\dfrac{11\pi}{6}\right)$.

Solution

$$
\begin{aligned}
z_1 z_2 &= \left[2\left(\cos\frac{2\pi}{3} + i\sin\frac{2\pi}{3}\right)\right]\left[8\left(\cos\frac{11\pi}{6} + i\sin\frac{11\pi}{6}\right)\right] \\
&= (2)(8)\left[\cos\left(\frac{2\pi}{3} + \frac{11\pi}{6}\right) + i\sin\left(\frac{2\pi}{3} + \frac{11\pi}{6}\right)\right] \\
&= 16\left[\cos\left(\frac{15\pi}{6}\right) + i\sin\left(\frac{15\pi}{6}\right)\right] \\
&= 16\left[\cos\left(\frac{\pi}{2}\right) + i\sin\left(\frac{\pi}{2}\right)\right] = 16i
\end{aligned}
$$

You can check this result by multiplying the original numbers as we learned earlier in the course. Finally, division is similar to multiplication, except that you subtract the angles and divide the absolute values.

Example 3: An Application of DeMoivre's Theorem

DeMoivre's theorem permits us to conveniently find powers of complex numbers. Use DeMoivre's theorem to calculate $\left(-1 + \sqrt{3}i\right)^{12}$.

Solution

We first find the trigonometric form of $-1 + \sqrt{3}i$. $r = \sqrt{(-1)^2 + \left(\sqrt{3}\right)^2} = \sqrt{1+3} = 2$.

We have $\tan\theta = \dfrac{b}{a} = \dfrac{\sqrt{3}}{-1} = -\sqrt{3} \Rightarrow \theta = \dfrac{2\pi}{3}$.

Now we can use DeMoivre's theorem.

$$\left(-1+\sqrt{3}i\right)^{12} = \left[2\left(\cos\frac{2\pi}{3}+i\sin\frac{2\pi}{3}\right)\right]^{12}$$

$$= 2^{12}\left[\cos\left((12)\frac{2\pi}{3}\right)+i\sin\left((12)\frac{2\pi}{3}\right)\right]$$

$$= 4096\left[\cos 8\pi + i\sin 8\pi\right] = 4096$$

Notice that we have just shown that one of the twelve 12th roots of 4096 is $-1+\sqrt{3}i$.

Study Tips

- Recall from our earlier work with complex numbers that we can graphically represent the complex number $a+bi$ as the ordered pair $(a,\ b)$ in the complex plane.

- If a complex number $a+bi$ is real $(b=0)$, then the absolute value is the usual absolute value $|a|$.

- The absolute value of a complex number represents its distance to the origin. For example, $\left|-1+3i\right| = \sqrt{(-1)^2 + 3^2} = \sqrt{10}$ means that the complex number $-1+3i$ is $\sqrt{10}$ units from the origin.

- The trigonometric form is often called the **polar form** of a complex number. We will study polar coordinates later in this course.

Pitfall

- The trigonometric form of a complex number is not unique. For example, you can add 2π to the angle θ and obtain another representation of the same complex number. And the number 0 has an infinite number of representations.

Problems

1. Plot the complex numbers $6i$ and $-2i$ in the complex plane, and find their absolute values.

2. Plot the complex numbers $-4+4i$ and $-5-12i$ in the complex plane, and find their absolute values.

3. Find the trigonometric form of the following complex numbers

    a. $5-5i$

    b. $\sqrt{3}+i$

    c. $-8i$

    d. 3

4. Calculate the product $\left[3\left(\cos\dfrac{\pi}{3}+i\sin\dfrac{\pi}{3}\right)\right]\left[4\left(\cos\dfrac{\pi}{6}+i\sin\dfrac{\pi}{6}\right)\right]$.

5. Calculate the quotient $\dfrac{\cos 50°+i\sin 50°}{\cos 20°+i\sin 20°}$.

6. Use DeMoivre's theorem to calculate $(2+2i)^6$.

7. Find the 3 cube roots of $64i$.

Systems of Linear Equations and Matrices

Lesson 25

Topics

- Systems of linear equations.
- The method of substitution.
- Gaussian elimination and elementary row operations.
- Matrix representation of a linear system.

Definitions

- Elementary row operations for systems of equations are defined as follows.

    o Interchange 2 equations.

    o Multiply one of the equations by a nonzero constant.

    o Add a multiple of one equation to another equation.

- Elementary row operations for matrices are defined as follows.

    o Interchange 2 rows.

    o Multiply a row by a nonzero constant.

    o Add a multiple of one row to another row.

Summary

This is the first of 4 lessons on solving systems of linear equations and matrices. We begin by using the method of substitution to solve a simple system of 2 equations and 2 unknowns.

Example 1: The Method of Substitution

Solve the following system of equations.

$$\begin{cases} x + y = 4 \\ x - y = 2 \end{cases}$$

Solution

We begin by solving for the unknown y in the first equation: $y = 4 - x$.

Then substitute this expression for y in the second equation: $x - y = 2 \Rightarrow x - (4 - x) = 2 \Rightarrow 2x = 6 \Rightarrow x = 3$.

Finally, we can solve for y: $y = 4 - x = 4 - 3 = 1$. The solution is $x = 3$, $y = 1$ or $(3, 1)$.

Example 2: Solving a System by Elimination

The method of elimination, known as the Gaussian elimination, is the preferred technique for solving systems of linear equations. The key step is adding a multiple of one equation to another equation in order to eliminate a particular variable. Solve the following system of equations.

$$\begin{cases} x - 2y + 3z = 9 \\ -x + 3y + z = -2 \\ 2x - 5y + 5z = 17 \end{cases}$$

Solution

We begin by adding the first equation to the second equation, producing a new second equation with the variable x eliminated. The first and third equations remain the same.

$$\begin{cases} x - 2y + 3z = 9 \\ y + 4z = 7 \\ 2x - 5y + 5z = 17 \end{cases}$$

Now add (-2) times the first equation to the third equation, eliminating the x-term in the third equation.

$$\begin{cases} x - 2y + 3z = 9 \\ y + 4z = 7 \\ -y - z = -1 \end{cases}$$

Add the second equation to the third equation, and then divide the third equation by 3.

$$\begin{cases} x - 2y + 3z = 9 \\ y + 4z = 7 \\ 3z = 6 \end{cases} \Rightarrow \begin{cases} x - 2y + 3z = 9 \\ y + 4z = 7 \\ z = 2 \end{cases}$$

Knowing the value of z, we can use back substitution to find the remaining unknowns, as follows.

$$z = 2 \Rightarrow y + 4(2) = 7 \Rightarrow y = -1$$
$$x - 2(-1) + 3(2) = 9 \Rightarrow x = 1$$

The solution is $x = 1,\ y = -1,\ z = 2$ or $(1,\ -1,\ 2)$.

Example 3: Matrix Representation of a Linear System

A convenient notation for systems of linear equations involves rectangular arrays of numbers called matrices. Notice how the following system of 3 equations in 2 unknowns is represented. The linear system $\begin{cases} x - 2y = 5 \\ 2x + 3y = 3 \\ 3x + y = 8 \end{cases}$ can be represented by the matrix $\begin{pmatrix} 1 & -2 & 5 \\ 2 & 3 & 3 \\ 3 & 1 & 8 \end{pmatrix}$.

The third column of the matrix is the right-hand side of the system, and the first 2 columns represent the coefficients of the unknowns x and y. You can use row reduction on the matrix just as you would do with the original system.

$$\begin{cases} x - 2y = 5 \\ 2x + 3y = 3 \\ 3x + y = 8 \end{cases} \Leftrightarrow \begin{pmatrix} 1 & -2 & 5 \\ 2 & 3 & 3 \\ 3 & 1 & 8 \end{pmatrix}$$

$$\begin{cases} x - 2y = 5 \\ 7y = -7 \\ 3x + y = 8 \end{cases} \Leftrightarrow \begin{pmatrix} 1 & -2 & 5 \\ 0 & 7 & -7 \\ 3 & 1 & 8 \end{pmatrix}$$

$$\begin{cases} x - 2y = 5 \\ 7y = -7 \\ 7y = -7 \end{cases} \Leftrightarrow \begin{pmatrix} 1 & -2 & 5 \\ 0 & 7 & -7 \\ 0 & 7 & -7 \end{pmatrix}$$

$$\begin{cases} x - 2y = 5 \\ y = -1 \\ 0 = 0 \end{cases} \Leftrightarrow \begin{pmatrix} 1 & -2 & 5 \\ 0 & 1 & -1 \\ 0 & 0 & 0 \end{pmatrix}$$

Hence, $y = -1$, and $x - 2(-1) = 5 \Rightarrow x = 3$. The solution is $(3,\ -1)$.

Study Tips

- An equation is linear if the variables occur to the first power.
- Solving systems of equations by hand involves a lot of arithmetic. Make sure you check your calculations as you go along. Fortunately, computers and graphing calculators have built-in programs for solving linear equations.
- For a system of linear equations, there are exactly 3 possibilities: a unique solution, no solution, or an infinite number of solutions.
- Some textbooks use vertical dots to separate the right-hand column of the matrix representing a linear system.

1. Solve the following systems by the method of substitution.

   a. $\begin{cases} 2x + y = 6 \\ -x + y = 0 \end{cases}$

   b. $\begin{cases} x - y = 0 \\ 5x - 3y = 10 \end{cases}$

2. Solve the following systems by the method of elimination.

   a. $\begin{cases} x + 2y = 4 \\ x - 2y = 1 \end{cases}$

   b. $\begin{cases} 2x - 5y = 0 \\ x - y = 3 \end{cases}$

   c. $\begin{cases} \dfrac{2}{5}x - \dfrac{3}{2}y = 4 \\ \dfrac{1}{5}x - \dfrac{3}{4}y = -2 \end{cases}$

   d. $\begin{cases} 2.5x - 3y = 1.5 \\ 2x - 2.4y = 1.2 \end{cases}$

3. Solve the following systems of linear equations by the method of elimination.

   a. $\begin{cases} x + y + z = 6 \\ 2x - y + z = 3 \\ 3x - z = 0 \end{cases}$

   b. $\begin{cases} 3x - 2y + 4z = 1 \\ x + y - 2z = 3 \\ 2x - 3y + 6z = 8 \end{cases}$

4. The University of Georgia and Florida State University scored a total of 39 points during the 2003 Sugar Bowl. The points came from a total of 11 scoring plays, which were a combination of touchdowns worth 6 points, extra points worth 1 point, and field goals worth 3 points. The same number of touchdowns and field goals were scored. How many touchdowns, extra points, and field goals were scored during the game?

Operations with Matrices

Lesson 26

Topics

- Matrices.
- Addition and scalar multiplication of matrices.
- Matrix multiplication.
- Applications to systems of linear equations.

Definitions

- A **matrix** is a rectangular array of numbers. $A = \begin{bmatrix} a_{ij} \end{bmatrix} = \begin{bmatrix} a_{11} & a_{12} & \cdots & a_{1n} \\ a_{21} & a_{22} & \cdots & a_{2n} \\ \vdots & \vdots & & \vdots \\ a_{m1} & a_{m2} & \cdots & a_{mn} \end{bmatrix}$. The order or size of a

  matrix is the number of rows and number of columns, $m \times n$.

- Two matrices are equal if they have the same order and corresponding entries are the same.

- The **sum** of 2 matrices of the same order is $\begin{bmatrix} a_{ij} \end{bmatrix} + \begin{bmatrix} b_{ij} \end{bmatrix} = \begin{bmatrix} a_{ij} + b_{ij} \end{bmatrix}$.

- The **scalar multiple** of a number times a matrix is $k \begin{bmatrix} a_{ij} \end{bmatrix} = \begin{bmatrix} k a_{ij} \end{bmatrix}$.

- A **zero matrix** is a matrix whose entries are all zero.

- An **identity matrix** is a square matrix of all zeros except for 1s down the main diagonal.

- If A is $m \times n$ and B is $n \times p$, then their **product** is an $m \times p$ matrix $AB = \begin{bmatrix} c_{ij} \end{bmatrix}$, where
  $c_{ij} = a_{i1}b_{1j} + a_{i2}b_{2j} + \cdots + a_{in}b_{nj}$.

Summary

In this lesson, we study operations with matrices: addition, scalar multiplication, and matrix multiplication. The sum of 2 matrices of the same size is simply the matrix obtained by adding the corresponding entries. The scalar multiple of a number times a matrix is obtained by multiplying the number (scalar) with each entry of the matrix. Both operations are illustrated in the first example.

Example 1: Addition and Scalar Multiplication of Matrices

Addition of 2 matrices of the same size: $\begin{bmatrix} 1 & 2 \\ 3 & 4 \end{bmatrix} + \begin{bmatrix} -1 & 0 \\ 2 & 4 \end{bmatrix} = \begin{bmatrix} 1-1 & 2+0 \\ 3+2 & 4+4 \end{bmatrix} = \begin{bmatrix} 0 & 2 \\ 5 & 8 \end{bmatrix}.$

A number times a matrix: $3\begin{bmatrix} 1 & 2 \\ 3 & 4 \end{bmatrix} = \begin{bmatrix} 3(1) & 3(2) \\ 3(3) & 3(4) \end{bmatrix} = \begin{bmatrix} 3 & 6 \\ 9 & 12 \end{bmatrix}.$

Observe that $A + 0 = A$, where 0 is the zero matrix of the same order as A.

Example 2: Matrix Multiplication

Matrix multiplication is more complicated than matrix addition or scalar multiplication. The product AB is defined if the number of columns of A equals the number of rows of B. Notice in this example how the rows of the left matrix are "multiplied" by the columns of the right matrix.

Find the product of the matrices $A = \begin{bmatrix} -1 & 3 \\ 4 & -2 \\ 5 & 0 \end{bmatrix}$ and $B = \begin{bmatrix} -3 & 2 \\ -4 & 1 \end{bmatrix}.$

Solution

$$AB = \begin{bmatrix} -1 & 3 \\ 4 & -2 \\ 5 & 0 \end{bmatrix}\begin{bmatrix} -3 & 2 \\ -4 & 1 \end{bmatrix} = \begin{bmatrix} (-1)(-3)+3(-4) & (-1)(2)+3(1) \\ 4(-3)+(-2)(-4) & 4(2)+(-2)(1) \\ 5(-3)+0(-4) & 5(2)+0(1) \end{bmatrix} = \begin{bmatrix} -9 & 1 \\ -4 & 6 \\ -15 & 10 \end{bmatrix}$$

Example 3: Matrix Multiplication and Linear Systems

You can conveniently use matrix multiplication to rewrite systems of linear equations. Rewrite the linear system $\begin{cases} x - 2y + z = 2 \\ 2x - y - z = 1 \end{cases}.$

Solution

We define the following matrices: $A = \begin{bmatrix} 1 & -2 & 1 \\ 2 & -1 & -1 \end{bmatrix}$, $B = \begin{bmatrix} 2 \\ 1 \end{bmatrix}$, $X = \begin{bmatrix} x \\ y \\ z \end{bmatrix}$. Then the original linear system can be represented by the simple matrix equation $AX = B$.

Study Tips

- You can use brackets or parentheses to denote matrices.
- The identity matrix I serves as the multiplicative identity: $AI = A$.
- In general, matrix multiplication is not commutative. But, it is associative: $A(BC) = (AB)C$.

Pitfalls

- Matrix equations can be confusing; be careful about the notation. For example, the scalar multiplication equation $0A = 0$ has 2 different zeros. The first zero is the real number zero, whereas the second zero is the zero matrix (of the same order as A).

- Matrix multiplication requires that the 2 matrices be of the appropriate sizes. For example, in Example 2 above, the product BA is not defined.

- Many familiar properties from algebra do not hold with matrices. For example, the cancellation law is not true in general: $AC = BC$, $C \neq 0$ does not imply $A = B$.

Problems

1. Find $3A - 2B$ if:

    a. $A = \begin{pmatrix} 1 & -1 \\ 2 & -1 \end{pmatrix}$ and $B = \begin{pmatrix} 2 & -1 \\ -1 & 8 \end{pmatrix}$.

    b. $A = \begin{pmatrix} 8 & -1 \\ 2 & 3 \\ -4 & 5 \end{pmatrix}$ and $B = \begin{pmatrix} 1 & 6 \\ -1 & -5 \\ 1 & 10 \end{pmatrix}$.

2. Find AB, if possible, where:

    a. $A = \begin{pmatrix} 2 & 1 \\ -3 & 4 \\ -1 & 6 \end{pmatrix}$ and $B = \begin{pmatrix} 0 & -3 & 0 \\ 4 & 0 & 2 \\ 8 & -2 & 7 \end{pmatrix}$.

    b. $A = \begin{pmatrix} 0 & -1 & 2 \\ 6 & 0 & 3 \\ 7 & -1 & 8 \end{pmatrix}$ and $B = \begin{pmatrix} 2 & -1 \\ 4 & -5 \\ 1 & 6 \end{pmatrix}$.

3. Find AB and BA, where:

    a. $A = \begin{pmatrix} 1 & 2 \\ 5 & 2 \end{pmatrix}$ and $B = \begin{pmatrix} 2 & -1 \\ -1 & 8 \end{pmatrix}$.

    b. $A = \begin{pmatrix} 3 & -1 \\ 1 & 3 \end{pmatrix}$ and $B = \begin{pmatrix} 1 & -3 \\ 3 & 1 \end{pmatrix}$.

4. Write the following system of equations as a matrix equation $AX = B$.

    a. $\begin{cases} -2x_1 - 3x_2 = -4 \\ 6x_1 + x_2 = -36 \end{cases}$

    b. $\begin{cases} x - 2y + 3z = 9 \\ -x + 3y - z = -6 \\ 2x - 5y + 5z = 17 \end{cases}$

5. Show that $(A + B)^2 \neq A^2 + 2AB + B^2$ does not hold for matrices.

6. If a and b are real numbers, then $ab = 0$ implies $a = 0$ or $b = 0$. Show that this property does not hold for matrices.

Inverses and Determinants of Matrices

Lesson 27

Topics

- Inverses of matrices.
- The inverse of a 2×2 matrix.
- Determinants.

Definitions and Formula

- The matrix B is the **inverse** of the square matrix A if $AB = BA = I$, where I is the identity matrix. A square matrix is singular if it does not have an inverse.

- The **determinant** of the 2×2 matrix $A = \begin{pmatrix} a & b \\ c & d \end{pmatrix}$ is $\det(A) = |A| = ad - bc$.

- **The matrix inverse algorithm** is used to find the inverse of the $n \times n$ square matrix A: Adjoin the $n \times n$ identity matrix and row reduce. If you are able to reduce A to I, then I will simultaneously reduce to the inverse $A^{-1} : \begin{bmatrix} A & \vdots & I \end{bmatrix} \rightarrow \begin{bmatrix} I & \vdots & A^{-1} \end{bmatrix}$. Otherwise, the matrix A doesn't have an inverse.

- The **formula for 2×2 matrices**: If $A = \begin{bmatrix} a & b \\ c & d \end{bmatrix}$, then $A^{-1} = \dfrac{1}{ad - bc} \begin{bmatrix} d & -b \\ -c & a \end{bmatrix}$ if $ad - bc \neq 0$.

Summary

In this lesson, we look at inverses and determinants of square matrices. The algorithm for calculating the inverse of a matrix, if it exists, relies on row reduction.

Example 1: Finding the Inverse of a Matrix

Find the inverse of the matrix $A = \begin{bmatrix} 1 & 4 \\ -1 & -3 \end{bmatrix}$.

Solution

First adjoin the identity matrix to A. $[A \ \vdots \ I] = \begin{bmatrix} 1 & 4 & \vdots & 1 & 0 \\ -1 & -3 & \vdots & 0 & 1 \end{bmatrix}$.

Then row reduce this rectangular matrix until we obtain the identity matrix on the left.

$$[A \ \vdots \ I] = \begin{bmatrix} 1 & 4 & \vdots & 1 & 0 \\ -1 & -3 & \vdots & 0 & 1 \end{bmatrix} \rightarrow \begin{bmatrix} 1 & 0 & \vdots & -3 & -4 \\ 0 & 1 & \vdots & 1 & 1 \end{bmatrix} = [I \ \vdots \ A^{-1}]$$

The inverse is the matrix on the right, $A^{-1} = \begin{bmatrix} -3 & -4 \\ 1 & 1 \end{bmatrix}$.

Example 2: The Inverse of a 2×2 Matrix

Calculating the inverse of a large matrix can be time consuming, and fortunately computers and calculators have built-in capabilities for matrix inversion. For small 2×2 matrices, there is a convenient formula for the inverse, if it exists.

The inverse of $A = \begin{bmatrix} 3 & -1 \\ -2 & 2 \end{bmatrix}$ is $A^{-1} = \dfrac{1}{3(2) - (-1)(-2)} \begin{bmatrix} 2 & 1 \\ 2 & 3 \end{bmatrix} = \dfrac{1}{4} \begin{bmatrix} 2 & 1 \\ 2 & 3 \end{bmatrix} = \begin{bmatrix} \frac{1}{2} & \frac{1}{4} \\ \frac{1}{2} & \frac{3}{4} \end{bmatrix}$.

The inverse of $A = \begin{bmatrix} 1 & 2 \\ 3 & 6 \end{bmatrix}$ does not exist because $ad - bc = 1(6) - 2(3) = 0$.

Example 3: Calculating Determinants

The expression $ad - bc$ in the previous example is called the determinant of the matrix. Determinants are defined for all square matrices and can be calculated with a graphing utility.

$$A = \begin{pmatrix} 2 & -3 \\ 1 & 2 \end{pmatrix} \Rightarrow \det A = 2(2) - (-3)(1) = 7$$

$$B = \begin{pmatrix} 2 & 1 \\ 4 & 2 \end{pmatrix} \Rightarrow \det B = 2(2) - 1(4) = 0$$

Study Tips

- If a matrix has an inverse, then the inverse is unique.
- If A is the inverse of B, then B is the inverse of A.
- A matrix is singular if and only if its determinant is zero.

Pitfall

- The notation for the inverse of a matrix, A^{-1}, does not mean the reciprocal of A, $\dfrac{1}{A}$.

Problems

1. Show that $B = \begin{pmatrix} 3 & -1 \\ -5 & 2 \end{pmatrix}$ is the inverse of $A = \begin{pmatrix} 2 & 1 \\ 5 & 3 \end{pmatrix}$.

2. Find the inverse of the following matrices, if it exists

    a. $A = \begin{pmatrix} 2 & 0 \\ 0 & 3 \end{pmatrix}$

    b. $A = \begin{pmatrix} 2 & 7 & 1 \\ -3 & -9 & 2 \end{pmatrix}$

    c. $A = \begin{pmatrix} 1 & 1 & 1 \\ 3 & 5 & 4 \\ 3 & 6 & 5 \end{pmatrix}$

    d. $A = \begin{pmatrix} -5 & 0 & 0 \\ 2 & 0 & 0 \\ -1 & 5 & 7 \end{pmatrix}$

3. Use the formula for the inverse of a 2×2 matrix to calculate the inverse of $\begin{pmatrix} 5 & 1 \\ -2 & -2 \end{pmatrix}$.

4. Use an inverse matrix to solve the system of linear equations $\begin{cases} x - 2y = 5 \\ 2x - 3y = 10 \end{cases}$.

5. Find the determinant of the following matrices.

    a. $\begin{pmatrix} 8 & 4 \\ 2 & 3 \end{pmatrix}$

    b. $\begin{pmatrix} -7 & 6 \\ \dfrac{1}{2} & 3 \end{pmatrix}$

6. Use a calculator to find the determinant of the matrix $\begin{pmatrix} -1 & 2 & -5 \\ 0 & 3 & 4 \\ 0 & 0 & 3 \end{pmatrix}$.

Applications of Linear Systems and Matrices

Lesson 28

Topics

- Cramer's rule.
- Applications of linear systems.
- Computer graphics.

Definition

- According to **Cramer's rule** if a system of n linear equations in n variables has a coefficient matrix A with a nonzero determinant $|A|$, then the solution of the system is $x_1 = \dfrac{|A_1|}{|A|}$, $x_2 = \dfrac{|A_2|}{|A|}$, $\ldots$, $x_n = \dfrac{|A_n|}{|A|}$, where the A_i has the same entries as A, except the column is the ith column of constants in the system of equations.

Summary

In this lesson, we look at some applications of systems of linear equations and matrices. Our first example illustrates Cramer's rule, a method for solving linear equations using determinants.

Example 1: Cramer's Rule

Use Cramer's rule to solve the linear system of equations $\begin{cases} 4x_1 - 2x_2 = 10 \\ 3x_1 - 5x_2 = 11 \end{cases}$.

Solution

Notice how the numerators are similar to the denominators, except for the substitution of the right-hand side.

$$x_1 = \frac{|A_1|}{|A|} = \frac{\begin{vmatrix} 10 & -2 \\ 11 & -5 \end{vmatrix}}{\begin{vmatrix} 4 & -2 \\ 3 & -5 \end{vmatrix}} = \frac{-28}{-14} = 2 \qquad x_2 = \frac{|A_2|}{|A|} = \frac{\begin{vmatrix} 4 & 10 \\ 3 & 11 \end{vmatrix}}{\begin{vmatrix} 4 & -2 \\ 3 & -5 \end{vmatrix}} = \frac{14}{-14} = -1$$

The solution is $(2, -1)$.

Example 2: An Application of Linear Systems

Many applications in science and engineering lead to systems of linear equations. This example illustrates how systems can be used to study automobile stopping distances.

During the testing of a new automobile braking system, the speeds x (in miles per hour) and the stopping distances y (in feet) were recorded as follows.

Speed x	Stopping Distance y
30	55
40	105
50	188

Fit a parabola to the data, and estimate the stopping distance for a speed of 70 miles per hour.

Solution

Let $y = ax^2 + bx + c$ be the equation of the parabola. To find the coefficients, we substitute the given data into this equation, producing a system of 3 equations and 3 unknowns.

$$\begin{cases} a(30)^2 + b(30) + c = 55 \\ a(40)^2 + b(40) + c = 105 \\ a(50)^2 + b(50) + c = 188 \end{cases}$$

Using Gaussian elimination, the solution is $a = 0.165$, $b = -6.55$, $c = 103$. Hence, the parabola is $y = 0.165x^2 - 6.55x + 103$. When $x = 70$, you obtain $y = 0.165(70)^2 - 6.55(70) + 103 = 453$ feet.

Example 3: Computer Graphics

Matrices are an important tool in the field of computer graphics. You can use 2×2 matrices and matrix multiplication to model simple transformations in the plane, as illustrated in this example.

The 2×2 matrix $T = \begin{pmatrix} -1 & 0 \\ 0 & 1 \end{pmatrix}$ represents a reflection in the y-axis because for any point $P = \begin{pmatrix} x \\ y \end{pmatrix}$ in the plane (written as a column), you have $TP = \begin{pmatrix} -1 & 0 \\ 0 & 1 \end{pmatrix} \begin{pmatrix} x \\ y \end{pmatrix} = \begin{pmatrix} -x \\ y \end{pmatrix}$. Similarly, the matrix $\begin{pmatrix} 1 & 0 \\ 0 & -1 \end{pmatrix}$ reflects points in the x-axis.

- Although the formula for Cramer's rule seems simple, it is not a practical method for solving systems of equations because of the need to evaluate determinants.
- In real-life applications, scientists often need to solve large systems of equations. Fortunately, computers are usually able to do this quickly and accurately. Moreover, graphing calculators have built-in programs for solving systems of linear equations.

Pitfall

- Cramer's rule only works for systems of n equations with n unknowns having a nonzero determinant. If the determinant of the coefficient matrix is zero, then the system has either no solution or infinitely many solutions.

Problems

1. Use Cramer's rule to solve (if possible) the following systems of equations.

   a. $\begin{cases} -7x + 11y = -1 \\ 3x - 9y = 9 \end{cases}$

   b. $\begin{cases} 3x + 2y = -2 \\ 6x + 4y = 4 \end{cases}$

2. You are offered 2 different jobs selling dental supplies. One company offers a straight salary commission of 6% of sales. The other company offers a salary of $350 per week plus 3% of sales. How much would you have to sell in a week in order to make the straight commission offer the better offer?

3. What are the dimensions of a rectangular tract of land if its perimeter is 40 miles and its area is 96 square miles?

4. A grocer sells oranges for $0.95 each and grapefruit for $1.05 each. You purchase a mix of 16 pieces of fruit and pay $15.90. How many of each type of fruit did you buy?

5. Describe the transformation given by the following matrices.

   a. $T = \begin{pmatrix} 0 & 1 \\ 1 & 0 \end{pmatrix}$

b. $T = \begin{pmatrix} 0 & -1 \\ 1 & 0 \end{pmatrix}$

6. Find the equation of the circle $x^2 + y^2 + Dx + Ey + F = 0$ that passes through the points $(0, 0)$, $(2, 2)$, and $(4, 0)$.

Circles and Parabolas

Lesson 29

Topics

- Conic sections.
- Circles.
- Parabolas.

Definitions

- A **conic section** is the intersection of a plane with a double-napped cone.

- A **circle** is the set of all points (x, y) in a plane that are equidistant from a fixed point (h, k), called the **center of the circle**. The distance r between the center and any point (x, y) on the circle is the **radius**.

- A **parabola** is the set of all points (x, y) in a plane that are equidistant from a fixed line, called the **directrix**, and a fixed point, called the **focus**, not on the line. The midpoint between the focus and the directrix is the **vertex**, and the line through the focus and the vertex is the **axis** of the parabola.

Formulas

- Standard form of a circle: $(x - h)^2 + (y - k)^2 = r^2$.

- Standard form of parabolas with vertex at (h, k):

  - Vertical axis; directrix $y = k - p$: $(x - h)^2 = 4p(y - k)$, $p \neq 0$.

  - Horizontal axis; directrix $x = h - p$: $(y - k)^2 = 4p(x - h)$, $p \neq 0$.

Summary

This is the first of 2 lessons on conic sections. In this lesson, we look at circles and parabolas; in the next lesson, we study ellipses and hyperbolas. All of these conic sections are defined as a set of points satisfying a certain property. Our first example deals with circles.

Example 1: Finding the Equation of a Circle

The point $(1, \ 4)$ is on a circle whose center is at $(-2, \ -3)$. Write the standard form of the circle.

Solution

The radius is the distance between the 2 points: $r = \sqrt{\left(1-(-2)\right)^2 + \left(4-(-3)\right)^2} = \sqrt{3^2 + 7^2} = \sqrt{58}.$

Using the standard equation of a circle, we have the following.

$$(x-h)^2 + (y-k)^2 = r^2$$
$$\left(x-(-2)\right)^2 + \left(y-(-3)\right)^2 = \left(\sqrt{58}\right)^2$$
$$(x+2)^2 + (y+3)^2 = 58$$

Example 2: Completing the Square

Find the standard equation of the circle given by $x^2 - 6x + y^2 - 2y + 6 = 0.$

Solution

In this example, we need to complete the square. Notice how we add and subtract appropriate constants to make the terms in the parentheses perfect squares. Write the equation as $\left(x^2 - 6x + ?\right) + \left(y^2 - 2y + ?\right) = -6.$ In order to complete the 2 squares, you need to add $\left(\dfrac{-6}{2}\right)^2 = 9$ to the first term and $\left(\dfrac{-2}{2}\right)^2 = 1$ to the second term. Make sure to also add these values to the right-hand side so as to not change the equation.

$$\left(x^2 - 6x + 9\right) + \left(y^2 - 2y + 1\right) = -6 + 9 + 1$$
$$(x-3)^2 + (y-1)^2 = 4$$

Example 3: Standard Form of the Equation of a Parabola

The standard form of the equation of a parabola permits us to analyze its focus and directrix. Find the standard form of the equation of the parabola with vertex at the origin and focus $(0, \ 4)$.

Solution

The axis is vertical and passes through the vertex $(0, 0)$ and focus $(0, 4)$. We also have $p = 4$. Hence,

$(x - h)^2 = 4p(y - k) \Rightarrow x^2 = 4py = 4(4)y = 16y$. The equation is $x^2 = 16y$ or $y = \dfrac{1}{16}x^2$.

Study Tips

- An important skill for analyzing conic sections is completing the square, as illustrated in Example 2.
- Circles are special cases of ellipses, which we study in the next lesson.
- If the center of the circle is at the origin, then its equation simplifies to $x^2 + y^2 = r^2$.

Problems

1. Find the standard form of the equation of the circle with center at the origin and radius $\sqrt{18}$.

2. Find the standard form of the equation of the circle if the point $(1, 0)$ is on the circle and the center is $(3, 7)$.

3. Find the standard form of the equation of the circle $x^2 + y^2 - 2x + 6y + 9 = 0$.

4. Find the standard form of the equation of the circle $4x^2 + 4y^2 + 12x - 24y + 41 = 0$.

5. Find the standard form of the equation of the parabola with vertex at the origin and focus at $\left(0, -\dfrac{3}{2}\right)$.

6. Find the standard form of the equation of the parabola with vertex at the origin and focus at $(-2, 0)$.

7. Find the vertex, focus, and directrix of the parabola $y^2 = -6x$.

8. Find the standard form of the equation of the parabola with vertex $(-2, 0)$ and focus $\left(-\dfrac{3}{2}, 0\right)$.

9. Find the standard form of the equation of the parabola with vertex $(0,\ 4)$ and directrix $y = 2$.

10. Each cable of the Golden Gate Bridge is suspended between 2 towers that are 1280 meters apart in the shape of a parabola. The top of each tower is 152 meters above the roadway. The cables touch the roadway midway between the towers. Write an equation that models the cables by placing the origin of the coordinate system at the center of the roadway.

Ellipses and Hyperbolas

Lesson 30

Topics

- Ellipses.
- Hyperbolas.

Definitions

- An **ellipse** is the set of all points (x, y) in a plane, the sum of whose distances from 2 distinct fixed points, called **foci**, is constant. The line through the foci intersects the ellipse at 2 points called **vertices**. The chord joining the vertices is the **major axis**, and its midpoint is the **center** of the ellipse. The chord perpendicular to the major axis at the center is the **minor axis**.

- The **eccentricity** of an ellipse is $e = \dfrac{c}{a}$.

- A **hyperbola** is the set of all points (x, y) in a plane, the difference of whose distances from 2 distinct fixed points, called **foci**, is a positive constant. The graph of a hyperbola has 2 branches. The line through the foci intersects the hyperbola at the **vertices**. The line segment joining the vertices is the **transverse axis**. The midpoint of the transverse axis is the **center**.

Formulas

- Standard form of ellipses with center at (h, k) and major and minor axes of lengths $2a$ and $2b$, respectively, where $0 < b < a$:

    o Horizontal major axis: $\dfrac{(x-h)^2}{a^2} + \dfrac{(y-k)^2}{b^2} = 1$.

    o Vertical major axis: $\dfrac{(x-h)^2}{b^2} + \dfrac{(y-k)^2}{a^2} = 1$.

    o The foci lie on the major axis, c units from the center, with $c^2 = a^2 - b^2$.

- Standard form of hyperbolas with center at (h, k):

    o Transverse axis is horizontal: $\dfrac{(x-h)^2}{a^2} - \dfrac{(y-k)^2}{b^2} = 1$.

o Transverse axis is vertical: $\dfrac{(y-k)^2}{a^2} - \dfrac{(x-h)^2}{b^2} = 1$.

o The vertices are a units from the center. The foci are c units from the center, with $c^2 = a^2 + b^2$.

Summary

In this lesson, we continue our study of conic sections by looking at ellipses and hyperbolas. Again, there are many applications of these conic sections, including orbits of planets and comets and whispering galleries. Our first example analyzes an ellipse centered at the origin.

Example 1: Sketching an Ellipse

Sketch the ellipse given by the equation $4x^2 + y^2 = 36$.

Solution

We first rewrite the equation in standard form.

$$4x^2 + y^2 = 36$$
$$\frac{x^2}{9} + \frac{y^2}{36} = 1$$
$$\frac{x^2}{3^2} + \frac{y^2}{6^2} = 1$$

As shown in figure 30.1, the center is $(0,\,0)$, and the major axis is vertical. $a = 6$, $b = 3$, and $c = \sqrt{6^2 - 3^2} = \sqrt{27} = 3\sqrt{3}$. The vertices are $(0,\,6)$ and $(0,\,-6)$, and the foci are $\left(0,\,3\sqrt{3}\right)$ and $\left(0,\,-3\sqrt{3}\right)$.

Figure 30.1

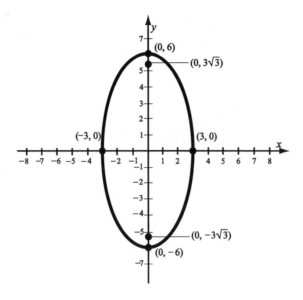

Example 2: A Whispering Gallery

Statuary Hall is an elliptical room in the United States Capitol Building in Washington DC. The room is also referred to as the Whispering Gallery because a person standing at one focus of the room can hear even a whisper spoken by a person standing at the other focus. Given that the dimensions of Statuary Hall are 46 feet wide and 97 feet long, find an equation for the shape of the floor. Assume that the center is at the origin.

Solution

We have $a = \dfrac{97}{2}$, $b = \dfrac{46}{2} = 23$, and $c = \sqrt{\left(\dfrac{97}{2}\right)^2 - 23^2} \approx 42.7$.

An equation for the ellipse is $\dfrac{x^2}{a^2} + \dfrac{y^2}{b^2} = 1 \Rightarrow \dfrac{x^2}{\left(97/2\right)^2} + \dfrac{y^2}{23^2} = 1$.

Example 3: Standard Form of the Equation of a Hyperbola

In this example, we analyze a hyperbola. Find the standard form of the equation of the hyperbola with foci $\left(-1,\ 2\right)$ and $\left(5,\ 2\right)$, and vertices $\left(0,\ 2\right)$ and $\left(4,\ 2\right)$.

Solution

The center of the hyperbola is the midpoint between the foci: $(2, 2)$. The transverse axis is horizontal, and $a = 2$, $c = 3$, and $b = \sqrt{c^2 - a^2} = \sqrt{9 - 4} = \sqrt{5}$. The equation is the following.

$$\frac{(x-h)^2}{a^2} - \frac{(y-k)^2}{b^2} = 1$$

$$\frac{(x-2)^2}{2^2} - \frac{(y-2)^2}{\left(\sqrt{5}\right)^2} = 1$$

Study Tips

- Circles are special cases of ellipses in which the 2 foci are the same.
- The eccentricity e, $0 < e < 1$, of an ellipse measures its "roundness." If $e \approx 1$, the ellipse is elongated, and if $e \approx 0$, the ellipse is more circular.
- The orbits of comets are elliptical, hyperbolic, or parabolic. For example, Halley's comet has an elliptical orbit.
- If the center of an ellipse is the origin, then its equation simplifies to either $\frac{x^2}{a^2} + \frac{y^2}{b^2} = 1$ or $\frac{x^2}{b^2} + \frac{y^2}{a^2} = 1$.
- If the center of a hyperbola is the origin, then its equation simplifies to either $\frac{x^2}{a^2} - \frac{y^2}{b^2} = 1$ or $\frac{y^2}{a^2} - \frac{x^2}{b^2} = 1$.

Pitfall

- Be careful to distinguish the formulas for ellipses and hyperbolas. There is a minus sign in the hyperbola formula.

Problems

1. Find the center, vertices, foci, and eccentricity of the following ellipses.

   a. $\frac{x^2}{64} + \frac{y^2}{9} = 1$

b. $\dfrac{(x-4)^2}{16} + \dfrac{(y+1)^2}{25} = 1$

c. $x^2 + 9y^2 = 36$

d. $9x^2 + 4y^2 + 36x - 24y + 36 = 0$

2. Find the standard form of the equation of the ellipse with vertices $(\pm 3, \, 0)$ and foci $(\pm 2, \, 0)$.

3. Find the eccentricity of the ellipse $\dfrac{x^2}{4} + \dfrac{y^2}{9} = 1$.

4. Find the center, vertices, and foci of the following hyperbolas

   a. $4x^2 - 9y^2 = 36$

   b. $9x^2 - y^2 - 36x - 6y + 18 = 0$

5. Find the standard form of the equation of the hyperbola with vertices $(2, \, 0)$ and $(6, \, 0)$, and foci $(0, \, 0)$ and $(8, \, 0)$.

Parametric Equations

Lesson 31

Topics

- Parametric equations.
- Eliminating the parameter.

Definitions

- If f and g are functions of the variable t on an interval $I,$ then the set of ordered pairs $(x, y) = (f(t), g(t))$ is a **plane curve** C. The equations given by $x = f(t)$ and $y = g(t)$ are **parametric equations** for the curve, and t is the **parameter**.

- As the parameter t increases, the curve is traced out in a specific direction called the **orientation** of the curve.

Formulas

- The parametric equations of the line through the 2 points (x_1, y_1) and (x_2, y_2) are $x = x_1 + t(x_2 - x_1)$, $y = y_1 + t(y_2 - y_1)$.

- **N**eglecting air resistance, the path of a projectile launched at a height h feet above the ground at an angle θ with the horizontal, and with initial velocity v_0 feet per second is $x = (v_0 \cos \theta)t$, $y = h + (v_0 \sin \theta)t - 16t^2$.

Summary

In this lesson, we look at parametric equations. Up to now, we have considered y as a function of the independent variable x, $y = f(x)$. Now both x and y will be functions of a third variable, say t. Each value of t generates an ordered pair $(x, y) = (x(t), y(t))$, as illustrated in the first example.

Example 1: Sketching a Plane Curve

Sketch the curve given by the parametric equations $x = t^2 - 4$, $y = \dfrac{t}{2}$, $-2 \le t \le 3$.

Solution

We first use the equations to generate some points on the curve. For example, when $t = -2$, $x = (-2)^2 - 4 = 0$ and $y = \dfrac{-2}{2} = -1$. Thus, the point $(0, \ -1)$ is on the graph. We can continue to calculate points, as indicted in the table.

t	-2	-1	0	1	2	3
x	0	-3	-4	-3	0	5
y	-1	$-\frac{1}{2}$	0	$\frac{1}{2}$	1	$\frac{3}{2}$

Now connect these points with a smooth curve to obtain the graph in figure 31.1. Note how the orientation is indicated by a small arrow.

Figure 31.1

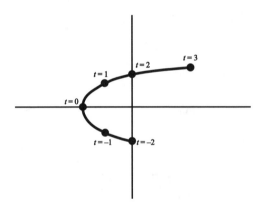

In this example, we can eliminate the parameter t: $t = 2y$, $x = t^2 - 4 = (2y)^2 - 4 = 4y^2 - 4$. We recognize this as the equation of a parabola.

Example 2: An Ellipse

In this example, we use our knowledge of trigonometry to trace out an ellipse. Eliminate the parameter, and sketch the curve represented by the parametric equations $x = 3\cos\theta$, $y = 4\sin\theta$. Notice that the parameter is θ, not t.

Solution

We have $\cos\theta = \dfrac{x}{3}$ and $\sin\theta = \dfrac{y}{4}$. From the fundamental trigonometric identity, we obtain

$\cos^2\theta + \sin^2\theta = \left(\dfrac{x}{3}\right)^2 + \left(\dfrac{y}{4}\right)^2 = 1 \Rightarrow \dfrac{x^2}{9} + \dfrac{y^2}{16} = 1$, which is the equation of an ellipse centered at the origin.

Example 3: Parametric Equations for a Line

In our final example, we develop the parametric equations for a line in the plane. This idea is very important for calculus, especially in 3 dimensions. Find a set of parametric equations for the line passing through the 2 points $(1,\ 4)$ and $(6,\ -3)$.

Solution

We use the equations for a line as follows.

$$x = x_1 + t(x_2 - x_1) = 1 + t(6-1) = 1 + 5t$$
$$y = y_1 + t(y_2 - y_1) = 4 + t(-3-4) = 4 - 7t$$

Notice in these parametric equations that when $t = 0$, $(x,\ y) = (1,\ 4)$, and when $t = 1$, $(x,\ y) = (6,\ -3)$.

Study Tips

- It is not always possible to eliminate the parameter, as we did in Example 1. Furthermore, the orientation is lost when the parameter is eliminated.
- The parametric equations for a curve are not unique. For instance, you could replace the parameter t with $2t$ to obtain a different set of equations.
- Graphing calculators have a built-in parametric mode. Try graphing the following *cycloid* on your graphing calculator: $x = \theta - \sin\theta$, $y = 1 - \cos\theta$.

Pitfall

- Parametric equations can be tricky. For example, the equations $x = t$, $y = t$ and the equations $x = t^2$, $y = t^2$ do not describe the same curve. The first curve is the line $y = x$, whereas the second curve is the ray $y = x$, $x \geq 0$.

1. Sketch the curve represented by the following parametric equations Then eliminate the parameter, and determine the corresponding rectangular equation.

    a. $x = t,\ y = -4t$

    b. $x = 3t - 3,\ y = 2t + 1$

    c. $x = t + 2,\ y = t^2$

    d. $x = 2\cos\theta,\ y = 3\sin\theta$

    e. $x = e^{-t},\ y = e^{3t}$

    f. $x = t^3,\ y = 3\ln t$

2. Eliminate the parameter and obtain the standard form of the equation of the circle given by $x = h + r\cos\theta,\ y = k + r\sin\theta$.

3. Eliminate the parameter and obtain the standard form of the equation of the ellipse given by $x = h + a\cos\theta,\ y = k + b\sin\theta$.

4. Use a graphing utility to graph the witch of Agnesi: $x = 2\cot\theta,\ y = 2\sin^2\theta$.

5. Use a graphing utility to graph the folium of Descartes: $x = \dfrac{3t}{1+t^3},\ y = \dfrac{3t^2}{1+t^3}$.

Polar Coordinates

Lesson 32

Topics

- Polar coordinates.
- Coordinate conversion.
- Polar equations and graphs.

Definition

- Let $P = (x, y)$ be a point in the plane. Let r be the distance from the origin O to P. Let θ be the angle from the positive x-axis to the segment OP. Then (r, θ) are the **polar coordinates** of the point (x, y).

Conversion Formulas

- The polar coordinates (r, θ) are related to the rectangular coordinates (x, y) as follows.

  o $x = r\cos\theta, \ y = r\sin\theta$

  o $\tan\theta = \dfrac{y}{x}, \ r^2 = x^2 + y^2$

Summary

In this lesson, we describe points and graphs in the plane using polar coordinates. The location of a point can be determined if we know its distance to the origin and the angle it makes with the positive x-axis, as illustrated in the first example.

Example 1: Plotting a Point in Polar Coordinates

The point $(r, \theta) = \left(3, -\frac{\pi}{6}\right)$ is graphed in figure 32.1. It is 3 units from the origin and makes an angle of $-\frac{\pi}{6}$ with the positive x-axis. This point can also be described by the polar coordinates $(r, \theta) = \left(3, \frac{11\pi}{6}\right)$.

Figure 32.1

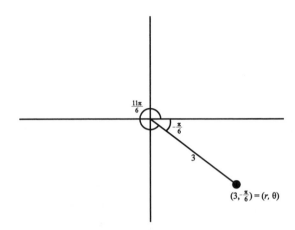

$\left(3, -\frac{\pi}{6}\right) = (r, \theta)$

Example 2: Polar to Rectangular Conversion

It is relatively easy to determine the rectangular coordinates of a point given in polar coordinates. If the polar coordinates of a point are $(r, \theta) = (2, \pi)$, then the rectangular coordinates are given by $x = r\cos\theta = 2\cos\pi = -2$, $y = r\sin\theta = 2\sin\pi = 0$. Hence, the rectangular coordinates are $(x, y) = (-2, 0)$.

Example 3: Rectangular to Polar Conversion

It is more difficult to convert from rectangular coordinates to polar coordinates than from polar coordinates to rectangular coordinates. If the rectangular coordinates of a point are $(x, y) = (-1, 1)$, then $\tan\theta = \dfrac{y}{x} = \dfrac{1}{-1} = -1 \Rightarrow \theta = \dfrac{3\pi}{4}$ because the point is in Quadrant II. Furthermore, $r^2 = x^2 + y^2 = 1 + 1 = 2$. So one set of polar coordinates is $(r, \theta) = \left(\sqrt{2}, \dfrac{3\pi}{4}\right)$.

Example 4: A Polar Equation

Many graphs are easily described using polar coordinates. Describe the polar graph $r = 2$.

Solution

This graph consists of all points at a distance 2 from the origin, which is a circle. You can confirm this if you convert to rectangular coordinates: $r = 2 \Rightarrow r^2 = 4 \Rightarrow x^2 + y^2 = 4$.

Study Tips

- Whereas the rectangular coordinates (x, y) are unique, polar coordinates are not, as illustrated in Example 1 above.
- Sometimes it is convenient to use negative values of r. For example, the following 3 polar representations of a point are equivalent: $\left(3, \frac{5\pi}{4}\right)$, $\left(3, \frac{-3\pi}{4}\right)$, $\left(-3, \frac{\pi}{4}\right)$.
- It is helpful to indicate which coordinate system you are using. For example, writing just $(-2, 0)$ does not tell you whether the coordinates are rectangular or polar. If you mean rectangular coordinates, then write $(x, y) = (-2, 0)$, which corresponds to $(r, \theta) = (2, \pi)$.
- When graphing polar curves, you might find it helpful to write down a table of values. Graphing utilities have a built-in polar mode, which uses radian measure.

Problems

1. Find the corresponding rectangular coordinates for the point $(r, \theta) = \left(-1, \frac{5\pi}{4}\right)$.

2. Find the corresponding rectangular coordinates for the point $(r, \theta) = \left(\sqrt{3}, \frac{5\pi}{6}\right)$.

3. Plot the point $(r, \theta) = \left(4, -\frac{\pi}{3}\right)$, and find the corresponding rectangular coordinates.

4. Plot the point $(r, \theta) = \left(-1, -\frac{3\pi}{4}\right)$, and find the corresponding rectangular coordinates.

5. Plot the point $(x, y) = (-7, 0)$, and find 2 sets of polar coordinates for the point with $0 \le \theta \le 2\pi$.

6. Plot the point $(x, y) = \left(-\sqrt{3}, -\sqrt{3}\right)$, and find 2 sets of polar coordinates for the point with $0 \le \theta \le 2\pi$.

7. Convert the following rectangular equations to polar forms.

   a. $x^2 + y^2 = 9$

   b. $y = 4$

   c. $x = 8$

8. Convert the following polar equations to rectangular form.

   a. $r = 4$

   b. $r = 2\cos\theta$.

9. Sketch the graph of the polar equation $r = 3(1 - \cos\theta)$.

Sequences and Series

Lesson 33

Topics

- Sequences.
- Limits of sequences.
- Summation notation.
- Series.
- Geometric series.

Definitions

- An **infinite sequence** is a function whose domain is the set of positive integers. The function values $a_1, a_2, a_3, \ldots, a_n, \ldots$ are the terms of the sequence.

- The **Fibonacci sequence** is defined by $a_0 = 1$, $a_1 = 1$, $a_k = a_{k-2} + a_{k-1}$, $k > 1$.

- **Factorial** notation: $n! = 1(2)(3)\cdots(n-1)(n)$. $0! = 1$.

- The **sum** of the first n terms of a sequence is represented by $\sum_{i=1}^{n} a_i = a_1 + a_2 + \cdots a_n$. The index of summation is i, n is the upper limit of summation, and 1 is the lower limit.

- The sum of the terms of an infinite geometric sequence is called an **infinite geometric series** or simply a **geometric series**.

Theorems

- Sum of a finite geometric series: $\sum_{i=0}^{n} r^i = \dfrac{1 - r^{n+1}}{1 - r}$.

- Sum of an infinite geometric series: $\sum_{i=0}^{\infty} r^i = \dfrac{1}{1 - r}$, $|r| < 1$.

  (If $|r| \geq 1$, the infinite series does not have a sum.)

Summary

Infinite sequences and series play a major role in calculus. Informally, an infinite sequence is a list of numbers, usually described by a rule or formula. Here are some examples.

Example 1: Writing the Terms of a Sequence

Write out the first 3 terms of the following sequences, beginning with $n = 1$.

1. $a_n = 3 + (-1)^n$

2. $a_n = \left(\dfrac{1}{2}\right)^n$

Solution

1. $a_1 = 3 + (-1)^1 = 2,\ a_2 = 3 + (-1)^2 = 4,\ a_3 = 3 + (-1)^3 = 2$

2. $a_1 = \left(\dfrac{1}{2}\right)^1 = \dfrac{1}{2},\ a_2 = \left(\dfrac{1}{2}\right)^2 = \dfrac{1}{4},\ a_3 = \left(\dfrac{1}{2}\right)^3 = \dfrac{1}{8}$

A key issue in the theory of sequences is that of limits. Informally, a sequence has a limit L if the terms of the sequence get arbitrarily close to L as n tends to infinity. In Example 1 above, the second sequence has limit 0, whereas the first sequence does not have a limit.

Example 2: The Fibonacci Sequence

The Fibonacci sequence is described by a recursive formula. Write out the first 8 terms of the Fibonacci sequence given that $a_1 = 1$, $a_2 = 1$, and $a_k = a_{k-2} + a_{k-1}$ for $k = 2,\ 3,\ 4,\ \dots$.

Solution

We know that the first 2 terms are 1 and 1. The third term is the sum of the first 2 terms, $a_3 = a_1 + a_2 = 1 + 1 = 2$. The fourth term is $a_4 = a_2 + a_3 = 1 + 2 = 3$. Continuing in this manner, you obtain 1, 1, 2, 3, 5, 8, 13, 21, ...

Example 3: Summation Notation

Summation notation is used to describe the sum of a finite number of terms of a sequence.

1. $\displaystyle\sum_{i=1}^{4} 3i = 3(1) + 3(2) + 3(3) + 3(4) = 3 + 6 + 9 + 12 = 30$

2. $\displaystyle\sum_{n=0}^{8} \dfrac{1}{n!} = \dfrac{1}{0!} + \dfrac{1}{1!} + \dfrac{1}{2!} + \dfrac{1}{3!} + \cdots + \dfrac{1}{8!} = 1 + 1 + \dfrac{1}{2} + \dfrac{1}{6} + \cdots + \dfrac{1}{40,320} \approx 2.71828$

Do you recognize the sum in this second example? If you were to add more and more terms, the sum would approach the number e.

Example 4: A Geometric Series

The theory of infinite series is major topic in calculus courses. One of the most familiar infinite series is the

geometric series: $\displaystyle\sum_{i=0}^{\infty}\left(\frac{1}{2}\right)^i = 1 + \frac{1}{2} + \frac{1}{4} + \frac{1}{8} + \cdots = \frac{1}{1-r} = \frac{1}{1-\left(\frac{1}{2}\right)} = 2.$

Study Tips

- It is often convenient to begin subscripting a sequence with n = 0 instead of $n = 1$ instead of In fact, a sequence can begin with any value of n. Furthermore, any convenient letter can be used as the index of summation.
- Graphing utilities have a built-in feature for calculating factorials. Try calculating 20! with your graphing utility. The answer will have 19 digits!
- The formula for a sequence is not unique. For example, the following 3 rules describe the same sequence of odd numbers.

    1. $a_n = 2n - 1$, $n = 1,\ 2,\ 3,\ ...$

    2. $b_n = 2n + 1$, $n = 0,\ 1,\ 2,\ ...$

    3. $c_n = 2n - 3$, $n = 2,\ 3,\ 4,\ ...$

Pitfall

- Real numbers can have multiple representations. For example, the number 1 is equal to the infinite decimal expansion $0.99999...$.

Problems

1. Write the first 5 terms of the following sequences. Assume n begins with 1.

    a. $a_n = 2n + 5$

    b. $a_n = \dfrac{n+1}{n}$

2. Write an expression for the apparent n^{th} term of the following sequences.

     a.   1, 4, 7, 10, 13, ...

     b.   0, 3, 8, 15, 24, ...

3. Simplify the following factorial expressions.

     a. $\dfrac{12!}{4!\,8!}$

     b. $\dfrac{(2n-1)!}{(2n+1)!}$

4. Find the following sums.

     a. $\displaystyle\sum_{i=1}^{5}(2i+1)$

     b. $\displaystyle\sum_{i=0}^{4}i^2$

5. Find the sum of the following infinite series.

     a. $\displaystyle\sum_{n=0}^{\infty}10\left(\frac{4}{5}\right)^n$

     b. $\displaystyle\sum_{n=0}^{\infty}5\left(-\frac{1}{2}\right)^n$

     c. $\displaystyle\sum_{n=1}^{\infty}2\left(\frac{7}{3}\right)^{n-1}$

Counting Principles
Lesson 34

Topics

- Counting principles.
- Permutations.
- Combinations.

Definitions

- Let E_1 and E_2 be 2 events. The first event, E_1, can occur in m_1 different ways. After E_1 has occurred, E_2 can occur in m_2 different ways. The **fundamental counting principle** says that the 2 events can occur in $m_1 m_2$ ways.

- A **permutation** of n elements is an ordering of the elements such that one element is first, one is second, one is third, and so on.

Formulas

- The number of permutations of n elements is $n! = n(n-1)(n-2)\cdots(3)(2)(1)$.

- The number of permutations of n elements taken r at a time is $_nP_r = \dfrac{n!}{(n-r)!}$.

- The number of combinations of n elements taken r at a time is $_nC_r = \dfrac{n!}{(n-r)!\,r!}$.

Summary

In this lesson, we develop some basic counting principles. This will lead into our next lesson on elementary probability. Our first example uses the fundamental counting principle.

Example 1: Using the Fundamental Counting Principle

How many different pairs of letters from the English alphabet are possible?

Solution

There are 2 events in this situation. The first event is the choice of the first letter, and the second event is the choice of the second letter. Since there are 26 letters in the English alphabet, there are $26 \times 26 = 676$ possible pairs of letters.

Example 2: Counting Horse Race Finishes

For permutations, order is important. Eight horses are running in a race. In how many ways can these horses come in first, second, and third? Assume no ties.

Solution

There are 8 choices for the winning horse, 7 for the second place horse, and 6 for the third place horse. The total number of ways is $8 \times 7 \times 6 = 336$. You could also use the formula for n permutations taken r at a time:

$$_8P_3 = \frac{8!}{(8-3)!} = \frac{8!}{5!} = \frac{8(7)(6)5!}{5!} = 8 \times 7 \times 6 = 336.$$

Example 3: Counting Card Hands

For combinations, order is not important. For example, in a poker hand, the order of the cards is not relevant. A standard poker hand consists of 5 cards dealt from a deck of 52. How many different poker hands are possible?

Solution

We use the formula for n combinations taken r at a time, along with a graphing utility. The number of hands is

$$_{52}C_5 = \frac{52!}{(52-5)!5!} = \frac{52(51)(50)(49)(48)47!}{47!5!} = \frac{52(51)(50)(49)(48)}{5!} = 2,598,960.$$

Study Tips

- Problems involving permutations and combinations require factorial calculations. Fortunately, these formulas are built into graphing calculators.

- Keep in mind that permutations involve order, whereas combinations do not.

1. Determine the number of ways a computer can randomly generate an odd integer from the integers 1 through 12.

2. Determine the number of ways a computer can randomly generate a prime number from the integers 1 through 12.

3. A customer can choose 1 of 4 amplifiers, 1 of 6 compact disc players, and 1 of 5 speaker models for an entertainment system. Determine the number of possible system configurations.

4. A college student is preparing a course schedule for the next semester. The student must select 1 of 2 mathematics courses, 1 of 3 science courses, and 1 of 5 courses from the social sciences. How many schedules are possible?

5. Evaluate $_8P_3$.

6. In how many ways can 5 children posing for a photograph line up in a row?

7. Evaluate $_4C_1$.

8. You can answer any 12 questions from a total of 14 questions on an exam. In how many ways can you select the questions?

9. As of June 2006, the U.S. Senate Committee on Indian Affairs had 14 members. If party affiliation is not a factor in selection, how many different committees are possible from the 100 U.S. Senators?

10. In Washington's Lottery game, a player chooses 6 distinct numbers from 1 to 49. In how many ways can a player select the 6 numbers?

Elementary Probability
Lesson 35

Topics

- Sample spaces.
- Probability.
- Mutually exclusive events.
- The complement of an event.

Definitions

- Any happening whose result is uncertain is called an **experiment**. The possible results of the experiment are **outcomes**. The set of all possible outcomes of the experiment is the **sample space** of the experiment, and any subcollection of a sample space is an **event.**

- If an event E has $n(E)$ equally likely outcomes and its sample space S has $n(S)$ equally likely outcomes, then the **probability** of event E is given by $p(E) = \dfrac{n(E)}{n(S)}$.

- Two events A and B (from the same sample space) are **mutually exclusive** if A and B have no outcomes in common.

- The **complement** of an event A is the collection of all outcomes in the sample space that are not in A, and is denoted A'.

Formulas

- If A and B are mutually exclusive events, then $P(A \cap B) = \varnothing$, and $P(A \cup B) = P(A) + P(B)$.

- If A and B are events in the same sample space, then the probability of A or B is $P(A \cup B) = P(A) + P(B) - P(A \cap B)$.

- The probability of the complement A'. of an event A is $P(A') = 1 - P(A)$.

Summary

In this lesson, we study elementary probability. Probability can be used to determine what are the chances of winning the lottery, or of rolling a 7 with 2 dic. To begin, we need to develop the concept of a sample space, as illustrated in the first example.

Example 1: Finding the Sample Space

Examples of finding the sample space include using a 6-sided die if it is tossed once. Its sample space is {1, 2, 3, 4, 5, 6}, and the sample space for tossing a coin once would be {H, T}

Example 2: Finding the Probability of an Event

To calculate the probability of an event, you need to use the formula $p(E) = \dfrac{n(E)}{n(S)}$. If 2 6-sided dice are tossed, what is the probability that a total of 7 is rolled?

Solution

There are 6 possible outcomes on each die, which means that there are $6 \times 6 = 36$ different outcomes when 2 dice are tossed. A 7 can occur 6 ways: $\{(1,\ 6),\ (2,\ 5),\ (3,\ 4),\ (4,\ 3),\ (5,\ 2),\ (6,\ 1)\}$.

Therefore, the probability of a total of 7 is $p(E) = \dfrac{n(E)}{n(S)} = \dfrac{6}{36} = \dfrac{1}{6}$.

Example 3: Mutually Exclusive Events

In this example, we develop the idea of mutually exclusive events. If 1 card is selected from a standard deck of 52 cards: 1. What is the probability that the card is either a king or a queen? 2. What is the probability that the card is either a heart or a face card?

Solution

1. The 2 events are mutually exclusive, so the answer is $\dfrac{4}{52} + \dfrac{4}{52} = \dfrac{8}{52} = \dfrac{2}{13}$.

2. The probability of selecting a heart (event A) is $\dfrac{13}{52}$. The probability of selecting a face card (event B) is $\dfrac{12}{52}$. However, 3 cards are both hearts and face cards (jack, queen, and king of hearts). So we have $P(A \cup B) = P(A) + P(B) - P(A \cap B) = \dfrac{13}{52} + \dfrac{12}{52} - \dfrac{3}{52} = \dfrac{22}{52} = \dfrac{11}{26} \approx 0.42$.

Example 4: The Complement of an Event

In this example we use the result of Example 2 to calculate the complement of an event. What is the probability of not getting a 7 when rolling 2 dice?

Solution

From Example 2, we know that the probability of getting a 7 when rolling 2 dice is $\frac{1}{6}$. Therefore, the probability of not getting a 7 is the complement, $1 - \frac{1}{6} = \frac{5}{6}$.

Study Tip

- The probability of an event is always a number between 0 and 1.

Pitfall

- Finding the probability of an event can be tricky. For example, suppose a couple intends to have 2 children. What is the probability that they will have one boy and one girl? The answer is $\frac{1}{2}$, not $\frac{1}{3}$, because the possible outcomes are $\{BB,\ GG,\ BG,\ GB\}$.

Problems

1. A coin and a 6-sided die are tossed. What is the sample space for this experiment?

2. A taste tester has to rank 3 varieties of orange juice, *A*, *B*, and *C*, according to preference. What is the sample space for this experiment?

3. A coin is tossed 3 times. What is the probability of getting exactly 2 tails?

4. A coin is tossed 3 times. What is the probability of getting at least 1 head?

5. Exactly 1 card is selected from a standard deck of 52 playing cards. What is the probability that the card is a face card?

6. Exactly 1 card is selected from a standard deck of 52 playing cards. What is the probability that the card is a face card or an ace?

7. A 6-sided die is tossed twice. What is the probability that the sum is 6?

8. A 6-sided die is tossed twice. What is the probability that the sum is less than 11?

9. The probability of event E is 0.75. What is the probability that the event will not occur?

10. Taylor, Moore, and Perez are candidates for public office. It is estimated that Moore and Perez have about the same probability of winning, and Taylor is believed to be twice as likely to win as either of the others. Find the probability of each candidate's winning the election.

11. A shipment of 12 microwave ovens contains 3 defective units. A vending company has ordered 4 of these units, and because all are packaged identically, the selection will be random. What is the probability that all 4 units are good?

GPS Devices and Looking Forward to Calculus
Lesson 36

Topics

- The Global Positioning System (GPS).
- Introduction to calculus: the tangent line problem.

Definition

- The **Global Positioning System (GPS)** is a set of 27 orbiting satellites, of which 24 are operational at any one time and 3 are backups. At any one time, at least 4 satellites are within view of a GPS device (receiver) from anywhere in the world.

Summary

In our final lesson, we look at 2 different topics. First, we study how the Global Positioning System (GPS) works. Then, we take a peek at calculus, and show how to find the equation of a tangent line to the graph of a function.

Example 1: Finding a Point of Intersection

The GPS requires a complicated analysis in 3 dimensions. Hence, we will simplify the discussion by considering a 2-dimensional system. Imagine that there are "satellites" at 3 points in the plane, as indicated in figure 36.1.

Figure 36.1

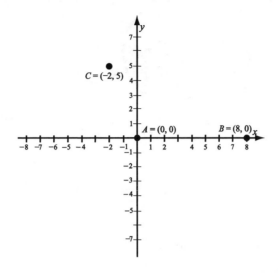

Suppose that my receiver indicates that I am 5 miles from satellite A at $(0, 0)$, 5 miles from satellite B at $(8, 0)$, and 10 miles from satellite C at $(-2, 5)$. Then my location is the point of intersection of the following 3 circles, as shown in figure 36.2.

1. $x^2 + y^2 = 25$

2. $(x-8)^2 + y^2 = 25$

3. $(x+2)^2 + (y-5)^2 = 100$

Figure 36.2

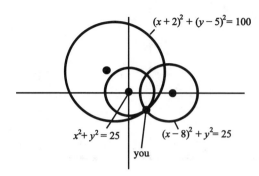

To find the point of intersection of these 3 circles, you can subtract equation 2 from equation 1 to obtain $x^2 - (x-8)^2 = 0 \Rightarrow x^2 - (x^2 - 16x + 64) = 0 \Rightarrow 16x - 64 = 0 \Rightarrow x = 4$. From equation 1, we see that $x = 4$ implies $y = \pm 3$.

Substitute $x = 4$ into equation 3: $(4+2)^2 + (y-5)^2 = 100 \Rightarrow (y-5)^2 = 64 \Rightarrow y - 5 = \pm 8 \Rightarrow y = 5 \pm 8 \Rightarrow y = 13$ or $y = -3$.

Hence, we see that $y = -3$, and our location is the point $(4, \ -3)$.

Example 2: Finding the Slope of a Tangent Line to a Curve

You know how to find the slope of a line in the plane. But how would you find the slope of a tangent line to a curve in the plane? This tangent line problem is the heart of the so-called differential calculus. Let's illustrate the tangent line problem with a specific example: Find the slope of the tangent line to the parabola $y = x^2$ at the point $P = (2, \ 4)$.

Solution

Let $Q = (x, \ x^2)$ be another point on the graph of the parabola, shown in figure 36.3.

Figure 36.3

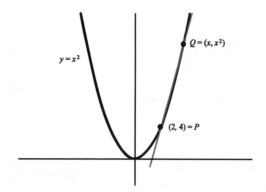

The slope of the line joining P and Q is $m = \dfrac{x^2 - 4}{x - 2} = \dfrac{(x-2)(x+2)}{x-2} = x + 2,\ x \neq 2$.

As the point Q gets closer to P, the value of x gets closer to 2, and the slope approaches 4. Calculus says that the slope of the tangent line at P is precisely 4.

Example 3: The Tangent Line to a Curve

We can use our knowledge of lines to find the equation of the tangent line at P. We know that the slope at $P = (2,\ 4)$ is 4, so the point-slope form of a line gives the following.

$$y - 4 = 4(x - 2)$$
$$y - 4 = 4x - 8$$
$$y = 4x - 4$$

Try graphing the parabola $y = x^2$ together with the tangent line $y = 4x - 4$ in the same viewing window of your graphing calculator.

Study Tips

- Determining the location of a receiver in space requires finding the point of intersection of a set of spheres rather than circles.

- The slope calculation of the tangent line in Example 2 can be expressed in limit notation:
$$\lim_{x \to 2}\left(\frac{x^2 - 4}{x - 2}\right) = \lim_{x \to 2}(x + 2) = 4.$$

- Notice that you needed your precalculus skills to find the solutions to both of these problems. You are ready to study calculus!

Problems

1. Your GPS device indicates that you are 5 miles from the point $A = (0, 0)$, 10 miles from the point $B = (-5, 2)$, and 5 miles from the point $C = (0, -8)$. Where are you located?

2. Find the equation of the tangent line to the graph of the parabola $f(x) = x^2$ at the point $(-3, 9)$.

Solutions

Lesson 1

1. **a.** $h(2) = 2^2 - 2(2) = 0$

   b. $h(1.5) = 1.5^2 - 2(1.5) = -0.75$

   c. $h(x+2) = (x+2)^2 - 2(x+2) = x^2 + 4x + 4 - 2x - 4 = x^2 + 2x$

2. **a.** $q(0) = \dfrac{1}{0^2 - 9} = -\dfrac{1}{9}$

   b. $q(3) = \dfrac{1}{3^2 - 9}$ is undefined because of division by zero.

   c. $q(y+3) = \dfrac{1}{(y+3)^2 - 9} = \dfrac{1}{y^2 + 6y}$

3. Domain: All real numbers except $t = 0$.

4. The term in the radical cannot be zero or negative. Hence, $y - 10 > 0 \Rightarrow y > 10$. Domain: All $y > 10$.

5. This is not a function of x. For example, $y = 2$ and $y = -2$ both correspond to $x = 0$.

6. This is a function of x. Its graph passes the vertical line test.

7. $A = \pi r^2$, $C = 2\pi r$

   $$r = \frac{C}{2\pi} \Rightarrow A = \pi \left(\frac{C}{2\pi} \right)^2 = \frac{C^2}{4\pi}$$

$$f(x) = \begin{cases} 2x + 3, & x < 0 \\ 3 - x, & x \geq 0 \end{cases}$$

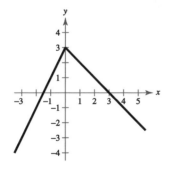

8. The graph of $y = \sqrt{x} + 2$ is the graph of $f(x) = \sqrt{x}$ shifted vertically upward 2 units.

9. The graph of $y = \sqrt{x-2}$ is the graph of $f(x) = \sqrt{x}$ shifted to the right 2 units.

Lesson 2

1. In slope-intercept form, the equation is $y = 5x + 3$. The slope is 5 and the y-intercept is $(0, 3)$.

    $$5x - y + 3 = 0$$
    $$y = 5x + 3$$

    (a) Slope: $m = 5$

    y-intercept: $(0, 3)$

    (b)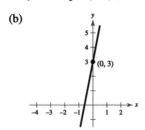

2. Using point-slope form, $y + 2 = 3(x - 0) \Rightarrow y = 3x - 2$.

3. The slope of the line is $\dfrac{5 - (-1)}{-5 - 5} = \dfrac{6}{-10} = -\dfrac{3}{5}$. The equation of the line is

    $$y + 1 = -\frac{3}{5}(x - 5) \Rightarrow y = -\frac{3}{5}x + 2.$$

4. $x^2 + 4x = 12$
    $x^2 + 4x - 12 = 0$
    $(x + 6)(x - 2) = 0$
    $x = -6,\ 2$

5. $-x^2 + 2x + 2 = 0,\ a = -1,\ b = 2,\ c = 2$

    $$x = \frac{-b \pm \sqrt{b^2 - 4ac}}{2a} = \frac{-2 \pm \sqrt{2^2 - 4(-1)(2)}}{2(-1)} = \frac{-2 \pm \sqrt{12}}{-2} = \frac{-1 \pm \sqrt{3}}{-1}$$

    $$x = 1 \pm \sqrt{3}$$

6. $x^2 + 4x = 32$
    $x^2 + 4x + 4 = 32 + 4$
    $(x + 2)^2 = 36$
    $x + 2 = \pm 6$
    $x = -2 \pm 6 \Rightarrow x = -8,\ 4$

    There are many correct answers. For example, $(x + 6)(x - 5) = 0 \Rightarrow x^2 + x - 30 = 0$. Or, another equation is $-x^2 - x + 30 = 0$.

7. $f(x) = (x-4)(x+3)(x-3)(x-0)$

$\quad\quad = (x-4)(x^2-9)x$

$\quad\quad = x^4 - 4x^3 - 9x^2 + 36x$

8. Using a graphic utility you see that the polynomial has 3 zeros. They are in the intervals $(-1, 0)$, $(1, 2)$, and $(2, 3)$. The approximate zeros are -0.879, 1.347, and 2.532.

9. $5x^3 + 30x^2 + 45x = 0$

$\quad\quad 5x(x^2 + 6x + 9) = 0$

$\quad\quad\quad 5x(x+3)^2 = 0$

$\quad\quad\quad\quad\quad x = 0,\ x = -3$

10. $x^4 - 4x^2 + 3 = 0$

$\quad (x^2 - 3)(x^2 - 1) = 0$

$\quad (x+\sqrt{3})(x-\sqrt{3})(x+1)(x-1) = 0$

$\quad x = -\sqrt{3},\ \sqrt{3},\ -1,\ 1$

11. Let x be the first number and y the second number. Then $x + 2y = 24 \Rightarrow x = 24 - 2y$. The product is $P = xy = (24 - 2y)y = 24y - 2y^2$. Completing the square,

$P = -2y^2 + 24y$

$\quad = -2(y^2 - 12y + 36) + 72$

$\quad = -2(y - 6)^2 + 72.$

12. The maximum value occurs at the vertex of the parabola and equals 72. This happens when $y = 6$ and $x = 24 - 2(6) = 12.$

Lesson 3

1. $13i - (14 - 7i) = 13i - 14 + 7i = -14 + 20i$

2. $\sqrt{-6}\sqrt{-2} = (\sqrt{6}i)(\sqrt{2}i) = \sqrt{12}i^2 = 2\sqrt{3}(-1) = -2\sqrt{3}$

3. $(1+i)(3-2i) = 3 - 2i + 3i - 2i^2 = 3 + i + 2 = 5 + i$

4. $4i(8+5i) = 32i + 20i^2 = 32i + 20(-1) = -20 + 32i$

5. $4 - 3i$ is the complex conjugate of $4 + 3i$.

$(4+3i)(4-3i) = 16 + 9 = 25$

6. $3 + \sqrt{2}i$ is the complex conjugate of $3 - \sqrt{-2} = 3 - \sqrt{2}i.$

$$\left(3-\sqrt{2}i\right)\left(3+\sqrt{2}i\right)=9+2=11$$

7. $\dfrac{2}{4-5i}=\dfrac{2}{4-5i}\cdot\dfrac{4+5i}{4+5i}=\dfrac{8+10i}{16+25}=\dfrac{8}{41}+\dfrac{10}{41}i$

8. By the quadratic formula, the zeros are $x=\dfrac{12\pm\sqrt{(-12)^2-4(26)}}{2}=6\pm\sqrt{10}.$

$$f(x)=\left[x-\left(6+\sqrt{10}\right)\right]\left[x-\left(6-\sqrt{10}\right)\right]=\left[x-6-\sqrt{10}\right]\left[x-6+\sqrt{10}\right]$$

9. $f(x)=x^4+10x^2+9=\left(x^2+1\right)\left(x^2+9\right)=(x-i)(x+i)(x+3i)(x-3i)$

The zeros are $x=\pm i,\ \pm 3i.$

10. Since $4-i$ is a zero, so is its conjugate $4+i$. Hence, you have the following.

$$\begin{aligned}f(x)&=(x-2)^2(x-4-i)(x-4+i)\\&=(x-2)^2\left(x^2-8x+16+1\right)\\&=\left(x^2-4x+4\right)\left(x^2-8x+17\right)\\&=x^4-12x^3+53x^2-100x+68\end{aligned}$$

11. The Mandelbrot sequence is $\dfrac{1}{2}i,\ \left(\dfrac{1}{2}i\right)^2+\dfrac{1}{2}i=-\dfrac{1}{4}+\dfrac{1}{2}i,\ -\dfrac{3}{16}+\dfrac{1}{4}i,\ -\dfrac{7}{256}+\dfrac{13}{32}i.$

This sequence is bounded, so the number is in the Mandelbrot set.

Lesson 4

1.   **a.** y-intercept: $\left(0,\ \dfrac{1}{2}\right)$; vertical asymptote: $x=-2$; horizontal asymptote: $y=0$.

$f(x)=\dfrac{1}{x+2}$

y-intercept: $\left(0,\dfrac{1}{2}\right)$

Vertical asymptote: $x=-2$

Horizontal asymptote: $y=0$

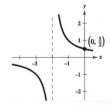

x	-4	-3	-1	0	1
y	$-\frac{1}{2}$	-1	1	$\frac{1}{2}$	$\frac{1}{3}$

b. *y*-intercept: $\left(0, -\dfrac{1}{6}\right)$; **vertical asymptote:** $x = 6$; **horizontal asymptote:** $y = 0$.

$f(x) = \dfrac{1}{x - 6}$

y-intercept: $\left(0, -\dfrac{1}{6}\right)$

Vertical asymptote: $x = 6$

Horizontal asymptote: $y = 0$

x	-1	0	2	4	8	10
y	$-\frac{1}{7}$	$-\frac{1}{6}$	$-\frac{1}{4}$	$-\frac{1}{2}$	$\frac{1}{2}$	$\frac{1}{4}$

c. Intercept: $(0,0)$; vertical asymptotes: $x = -2,\ 2$; horizontal asymptote: $y = 1$.

$f(x) = \dfrac{x^2}{x^2 - 4}$

Intercept: $(0, 0)$

Vertical asymptotes: $x = 2,\ x = -2$

Horizontal asymptote: $y = 1$

y-axis symmetry

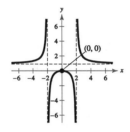

x	-4	-1	0	-1	4
y	$\frac{4}{3}$	$-\frac{1}{3}$	0	$-\frac{1}{3}$	$\frac{4}{3}$

d. $f(x) = \dfrac{x^2 + 3x}{x^2 + x - 6} = \dfrac{x(x+3)}{(x-2)(x+3)} = \dfrac{x}{x-2}, \; x \neq -3$

$f(x) = \dfrac{x^2 + 3x}{x^2 + x - 6} = \dfrac{x(x+3)}{(x-2)(x+3)} = \dfrac{x}{x-2},$

$x \neq -3$

Intercept: $(0, 0)$

Vertical asymptote: $x = 2$

(There is a hole at $x = -3$.)

Horizontal asymptote: $y = 1$

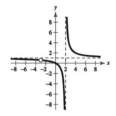

x	-2	-1	0	1	2	3
y	$\frac{1}{2}$	$\frac{1}{3}$	0	-1	Undef.	3

Intercept: $(0, 0)$; vertical asymptote: $x = 2$; horizontal asymptote: $y = 1$.

There is a hole at $\left(-3, \; \dfrac{3}{5}\right)$.

2. a. Horizontal asymptote: $y = 0$; vertical asymptote: $x = 0$.

b. $f(x) = \dfrac{x^2 - 25}{x^2 + 5x} = \dfrac{(x-5)(x+5)}{x(x+5)} = \dfrac{x-5}{x}, \; x \neq -5$

Horizontal asymptote: $y = 1$; vertical asymptote: $x = 0$. (Hole at $(-5, \; 2)$.)

3. $f(x) = \dfrac{(x-2)(x+2)}{x+3}$

The zeros are the zeros of the numerator: $x = \pm 2$.

4. $f(x) = \dfrac{x-1}{(x-2)(x^2 + 1)}$ is one possible answer.

5. a. There are 2 horizontal asymptotes: $y = \pm 6$.

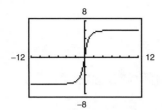

b. There are 2 horizontal asymptotes at $y = \pm 4$ and one vertical asymptote at $x = -1$.

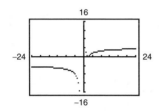

Lesson 5

1. a. $(f+g)(x) = x^2 + 5 + \sqrt{1-x}$

b. $(f-g)(x) = x^2 + 5 - \sqrt{1-x}$

c. $(fg)(x) = (x^2 + 5)\sqrt{1-x}$

d. $\left(\dfrac{f}{g}\right)(x) = \dfrac{x^2 + 5}{\sqrt{1-x}}$

2. a. The domain of f is $x + 4 \geq 0$ or $x \geq -4$.

b. The domain of g is all real numbers.

c. $(f \circ g)(x) = f(g(x)) = f(x^2) = \sqrt{x^2 + 4}$

The domain is all real numbers.

3. By inspection, the inverse is $g(x) = \dfrac{x}{6}$.

4. By inspection, the inverse is $g(x) = x + 3$.

5. $f(g(x)) = f\left(\sqrt[3]{x-5}\right) = \left(\sqrt[3]{x-5}\right)^3 + 5 = (x-5) + 5 = x$

$g(f(x)) = g\left(x^3 + 5\right) = \sqrt[3]{\left(x^3 + 5\right) - 5} = \sqrt[3]{x^3} = x$

6. The function is not one-to-one. For example, $f(1) = f(-1) = 1$. The graph does not pass the horizontal line test.

7. This function is one-to-one. The graph passes the horizontal line test.

8. $y = 2x - 3$

$x = 2y - 3$

$y = \dfrac{x+3}{2}$

$f^{-1}(x) = \dfrac{x+3}{2}$

The graphs are reflections of each other in the line $y = x$.

9. $y = \sqrt{4 - x^2},\ 0 \le x \le 2$

$x = \sqrt{4 - y^2},\ 0 \le y \le 2,\ 0 \le x \le 2$

$x^2 = 4 - y^2$

$y^2 = 4 - x^2$

$y = \sqrt{4 - x^2}$

$f^{-1}(x) = \sqrt{4 - x^2},\ 0 \le x \le 2$

The graphs are reflections of each other in the line $y = x$.

10. If we let $f(x) = |x + 2|,\ x \ge -2$, then f has an inverse. (Note: we could have also let $x \le -2$.)

$y = |x + 2| = x + 2,\ x \ge -2$

$x = y + 2$

$y = x - 2$

$f^{-1}(x) = x - 2,\ x \ge 0$

The domain of f is $x \ge -2$, and the range is $y \ge 0$. The domain of f^{-1} is $x \ge 0$, and the range is $y \ge -2$.

Lesson 6

1. **a.** The domain is $x \geq 5$ or $[5, \infty)$.

   b. $x^2 - 4 \geq 0$ implies $x \geq 2$ or $x \leq -2$. The domain is $(-\infty, -2] \cup [2, \infty)$.

2. **a.** $-10 < 40$

   $$-\frac{1}{10}(-10x) > -\frac{1}{10}(40)$$
   $$x > -4$$

   b. $4(x+1) < 2x+3$
   $$4x+4 < 2x+3$$
   $$2x < -1$$
   $$x < -\frac{1}{2}$$

   c. $-8 \leq 1 - 3(x-2) < 13$
   $$-8 \leq 1 - 3x + 6 < 13$$
   $$-8 \leq -3x + 7 < 13$$
   $$-15 \leq -3x < 6$$
   $$5 \geq x > -2 \Rightarrow -2 < x \leq 5$$

   d. $0 \leq \dfrac{x+3}{2} < 5$
   $$0 \leq x + 3 < 10$$
   $$-3 \leq x < 7$$

   e. $|x-7| < 6$
   $$-6 < x - 7 < 6$$
   $$1 < x < 13$$

   f. $|x+14| + 3 > 17$
   $$|x+14| > 14$$
   $$x + 14 > 14 \quad \text{or} \quad x + 14 < -14$$
   $$x > 0 \quad \text{or} \quad x < -28$$

3. $x^2 - 4x - 5 > 0$
   $$(x-5)(x+1) > 0$$
   Testing the intervals $(-\infty, -1)$, $(-1, 5)$, and $(5, \infty)$, we have $x^2 - 4x - 5 > 0$ on $(-\infty, -1)$ and $(5, \infty)$, and $x^2 - 4x - 5 < 0$ on $(-1, 5)$.

4. $|x-7| \leq 10$

5. $|x-3| \geq 5$

Lesson 7

1. **a.** $4^2(3) = 16(3) = 48$

  b. $3(3^3) = 3(27) = 81$

2. **a.** $\dfrac{3}{3^{-4}} = 3^{1+4} = 3^5 = 243$

  b. $24(-2)^{-5} = \dfrac{24}{(-2)^5} = \dfrac{24}{-32} = -\dfrac{3}{4}$

3. **a.** Horizontal asymptote: $y = 0$; intercept: $(0,\,1)$; increasing.

  $g(x) = 5^x$

x	-2	-1	0	1	2
y	$\frac{1}{25}$	$\frac{1}{5}$	1	5	25

  Asymptote: $y = 0$
  Intercept: $(0, 1)$
  Increasing

  b. Horizontal asymptote: $y = 0$; intercept: $(0,\,1)$; decreasing.

  7. $f(x) = \left(\frac{1}{5}\right)^x = 5^{-x}$

x	-2	-1	0	1	2
y	25	5	1	$\frac{1}{5}$	$\frac{1}{25}$

  Asymptote: $y = 0$
  Intercept: $(0, 1)$
  Decreasing

4. The graph of g is a horizontal shift of 5 units to the right.

5. The graph of g is a reflection in the x-axis followed by a vertical shift 5 units upward.

6. $50e^{4(0.02)} = 50e^{0.08} \approx 54.164$

7. **a.** Asymptote: $y = 0$; intercept: $(0, 1)$; decreasing.

$f(x) = e^{-x}$

x	-2	-1	0	1	2
$f(x)$	7.39	2.72	1	0.37	0.14

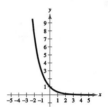

Asymptote: $y = 0$

b. Asymptote: $y = 2$; intercept: $\left(0, \ 2 + e^{-5}\right) \approx (0, \ 2.007)$; increasing.

$f(x) = 2 + e^{x-5}$

x	3	4	5	6	7
$f(x)$	2.14	2.37	3	4.72	9.39

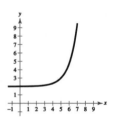

Asymptote: $y = 2$

8. **a.** $A = P\left(1 + \dfrac{r}{n}\right)^{nt} = 2500\left(1 + \dfrac{0.025}{1}\right)^{1(10)} \approx \$3200.21$

b. $A = P\left(1 + \dfrac{r}{n}\right)^{nt} = 2500\left(1 + \dfrac{0.025}{365}\right)^{365(10)} \approx \$3210.04$

c. $A = Pe^{rt} = 2500e^{0.025(10)} \approx \$3210.06$

Lesson 8

1. **a.** $\log_4 64 = 3 \Rightarrow 4^3 = 64$

b. $\log_{32} 4 = \dfrac{2}{5} \Rightarrow 32^{2/5} = 4$

2. $\log_2 16 = \log_2 2^4 = 4$

3. $\log_{10}\left(\dfrac{1}{1000}\right) = \log_{10}\left(10^{-3}\right) = -3$

4. $\log_{10} 345 \approx 2.538$

5. $\ln \sqrt{42} \approx 1.869$

6. $x = \log_6 6^2 = 2\log_6 6 = 2(1) = 2$

7. The functions f and g are inverses of each other.

   $f(x) = 3^x$ and $g(x) = \log_3 x$ are inverses of each other.

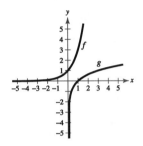

8. **a.** Domain: $x > -2$; vertical asymptote: $x = -2$; intercept: $(-1,\ 0)$.

   $y = \log_2(x + 2)$

   Domain: $x + 2 > 0 \Rightarrow x > -2$

   Vertical asymptote: $x = -2$

   $\log_2(x + 2) = 0$

   $\qquad x + 2 = 1$

   $\qquad\quad x = -1$

   x-intercept: $(-1, 0)$

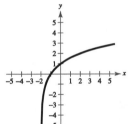

b. Domain: $x > -1$; vertical asymptote: $x = -1$; intercept: $(0,\ 0)$.

$h(x) = \ln(x + 1)$

Domain: $x + 1 > 0 \implies x > -1$

The domain is $(-1, \infty)$.

Vertical asymptote: $x + 1 = 0 \implies x = -1$

x-intercept: $\ln(x + 1) = 0$

$$e^0 = x + 1$$

$$1 = x + 1$$

$$0 = x$$

The x-intercept is $(0, 0)$.

$y = \ln(x + 1) \implies e^y - 1 = x$

x	-0.39	0	1.72	6.39	19.09
y	$-\frac{1}{2}$	0	1	2	3

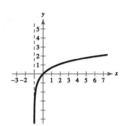

c. Domain: $x < 0$; vertical asymptote: $x = 0$; intercept: $(-1,\ 0)$.

$g(x) = \ln(-x)$

Domain: $-x > 0 \implies x < 0$

The domain is $(-\infty, 0)$.

Vertical asymptote: $-x = 0 \implies x = 0$

x-intercept: $\quad 0 = \ln(-x)$

$$e^0 = -x$$

$$-1 = x$$

The x-intercept is $(-1, 0)$.

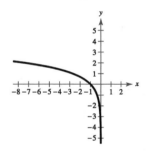

Lesson 9

1. **a.** $\log_3 7 = \dfrac{\ln 7}{\ln 3} \approx \dfrac{1.9459}{1.0986} \approx 1.771$

b. $\log_{15} 1460 = \dfrac{\ln 1460}{\ln 15} \approx \dfrac{7.2862}{2.7081} \approx 2.691$

2. **a.** $\ln 20 = \ln(4 \cdot 5) = \ln 4 + \ln 5$

b. $\ln \dfrac{5}{64} = \ln 5 - \ln 64 = \ln 5 - \ln 4^3 = \ln 5 - 3\ln 4$

3. **a.** $\log_4 8 = \ln_4 2^3 = 3\ln_4 2 = 3\ln_4 (4)^{\frac{1}{2}} = 3\left(\dfrac{1}{2}\right)\ln_4 4 = \dfrac{3}{2}$

b. $\ln\left(5e^6\right) = \ln 5 + \ln e^6 = \ln 5 + 6\ln e = \ln 5 + 6$

4. $\ln \sqrt{z} = \ln z^{1/2} = \dfrac{1}{2} \ln z$

5. $\ln x - 3\ln(x+1) = \ln x - \ln (x+1)^3 = \ln \dfrac{x}{(x+1)^3}$

6. $\log_3 9 = \log_3 3^2 = 2 \log_3 3 = 2(1) = 2$

7. $\ln e^3 - \ln e^7 = 3\ln e - 7\ln e = 3 - 7 = -4$

Lesson 10

1. **a.** $4^x = 16 = 4^2 \Rightarrow x = 2$

   b. $\left(\dfrac{1}{8}\right)^x = 64 \Rightarrow 8^{-x} = 8^2 \Rightarrow -x = 2 \Rightarrow x = -2$

2. **a.** $\ln x = -7 \Rightarrow x = e^{-7}$

   b. $\ln(2x-1) = 5 \Rightarrow 2x-1 = e^5 \Rightarrow 2x = 1 + e^5 \Rightarrow x = \dfrac{1}{2}\left(1 + e^5\right)$

3. **a.** $8^{3x} = 360 \Rightarrow \ln 8^{3x} = 3x \ln 8 = \ln 360 \Rightarrow x = \dfrac{\ln 360}{3\ln 8} \approx 0.944$

   b. $\left(1 + \dfrac{0.10}{12}\right)^{12t} = 2$

   $\left(\dfrac{12.1}{12}\right)^{12t} = 2$

   $12t \ln \dfrac{12.1}{12} = \ln 2$

   $t = \dfrac{1}{12} \dfrac{\ln 2}{\ln\left(12.1/12\right)} \approx 6.960$

   c. $e^{2x} - 4e^x - 5 = 0$

   $e^x = 5 \Rightarrow x = \ln 5 \approx 1.609$

   $e^x = -1$, impossible.

   d. $e^x = e^{x^2 - 2} \Rightarrow x = x^2 - 2$

   $x^2 - x - 2 = 0$

   $(x-2)(x+1) = 0$

   $x = 2, \ -1$

4. **a.** $\log_5 (3x + 2) = \log_5 (6 - x)$

$3x + 2 = 6 - x$

$4x = 4$

$x = 1$

b. $\log_4 x - \log_4 (x - 1) = \dfrac{1}{2}$

$\log_4 \left(\dfrac{x}{x-1} \right) = \dfrac{1}{2}$

$\dfrac{x}{x-1} = 4^{\frac{1}{2}} = 2$

$x = 2(x - 1) = 2x - 2$

$x = 2$

5. Using a graphing utility, graph the function $y = \log_{10} x - x^3 + 3$. You will obtain the 2 zeros, $x \approx 1.469$ and $x \approx 0.001$.

Lesson 11

1. We want to find the time needed for the amount to reach $20,000.

$20,000 = 10,000 e^{0.035t}$

$2 = e^{0.035t}$

$\ln 2 = 0.035t$

$t = \dfrac{\ln 2}{0.035} \approx 19.8$ years

2. Let C be the initial amount. We first use the half-life information to calculate the value of k.

$\dfrac{1}{2} C = C e^{k(1599)} \Rightarrow \dfrac{1}{2} = e^{1599k}$

$\ln \dfrac{1}{2} = 1599k \Rightarrow k = \dfrac{\ln (1/2)}{1599}$

Now we can use the decay model to find the amount after 1000 years.

$y = C e^{kt} = 10 e^{\left[\ln(1/2)/1599 \right]1000} \approx 6.48$ grams

3. a. $180 = 134.0e^{k(10)}$

$$\frac{180}{134.0} = e^{10k}$$

$$10k = \ln\frac{180}{134.0} \Rightarrow k \approx 0.0295$$

b. For 2010, $t = 20$ and $P = 134.0e^{20k} \approx 241,734$ people.

4. a.

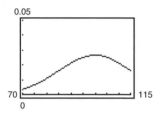

b. The maximum point is 100, the average IQ score.

5. a.
$$p(5) = \frac{1000}{1+9e^{-0.1656(5)}} \approx 203 \text{ animals}$$

$$500 = \frac{1000}{1+9e^{-0.1656(t)}} \Rightarrow 1+9e^{-0.1656(t)} = 2 \Rightarrow e^{-0.1656(t)} = \frac{1}{9}$$

$$-0.1656t = \ln\frac{1}{9} \Rightarrow t = \frac{\ln\left(\frac{1}{9}\right)}{-0.1656} \approx 13 \text{ months}$$

b. The horizontal asymptotes occur at p = 1000 and p = 0. The asymptote at p = 1000 means that there will not be more than 1000 animals in the preserve. As time goes on, the population approaches 1000 animals.

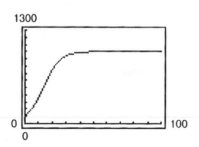

Lesson 12

1. **a.** Since $90° < 150° < 180°$, $150°$ lies in Quadrant II.

    b. Since $270° < 282° < 360°$, $282°$ lies in Quadrant IV.

    c. Since $0 < \dfrac{\pi}{5} < \dfrac{\pi}{2}$, $\dfrac{\pi}{5}$ lies in Quadrant I.

    d. Since $\pi < \dfrac{7\pi}{5} < \dfrac{3\pi}{2}$, $\dfrac{7\pi}{5}$ lies in Quadrant III.

(a) 30°

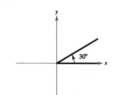

(b) −150°

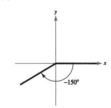

(c)

(d)

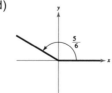

2. a. $-495° + 360° = -135°$

$-495° + 720° = 225°$

b. $230° + 360° = 590°$

$230° - 360° = -130°$

3. a. $-\dfrac{9\pi}{4} + 4\pi = \dfrac{7\pi}{4}$

$-\dfrac{9\pi}{4} + 2\pi = -\dfrac{\pi}{4}$

b. $-\dfrac{2\pi}{15} + 2\pi = \dfrac{28\pi}{4}$

$-\dfrac{2\pi}{15} - 2\pi = -\dfrac{32\pi}{15}$

4. a. Complement of $24°$: $90° - 24° = 66°$; supplement: $180° - 24° = 156°$.

b. Complement of $126°$ not possible; supplement: $180° - 126° = 54°$.

c. Complement of $\dfrac{\pi}{3}$: $\dfrac{\pi}{2} - \dfrac{\pi}{3} = \dfrac{\pi}{6}$; supplement: $\pi - \dfrac{\pi}{3} = \dfrac{2\pi}{3}$.

d. Complement of $\dfrac{3\pi}{4}$ not possible; supplement: $\pi - \dfrac{3\pi}{4} = \dfrac{\pi}{4}$.

5. a. $30° = 30\left(\dfrac{\pi}{180°}\right) = \dfrac{\pi}{6}$

b. $150° = 150\left(\dfrac{\pi}{180°}\right) = \dfrac{5\pi}{6}$

6. a. $\dfrac{3\pi}{2} = \dfrac{3\pi}{2}\left(\dfrac{180°}{\pi}\right) = 270°$

b. $-\dfrac{7\pi}{6} = -\dfrac{7\pi}{6}\left(\dfrac{180°}{\pi}\right) = -210°$

7. $s = r\theta \Rightarrow 8 = 29\theta \Rightarrow \theta = \dfrac{8}{29}$ radians

8. $s = r\theta \Rightarrow s = 2(1) = 2$ meters

9. $r = \dfrac{s}{\theta} = \dfrac{36}{\pi/2} = \dfrac{72}{\pi}$ feet ≈ 22.92 feet

10. $\theta = \dfrac{s}{r} = \dfrac{450}{6378} \approx 0.07056$ radian $\approx 4.04° \approx 4°\ 2'\ 33.02''$

Lesson 13

1. **a.** $b = \sqrt{13^2 - 5^2} = \sqrt{169 - 25} = \sqrt{144} = 12$

$\sin\theta = \dfrac{\text{opp}}{\text{hyp}} = \dfrac{5}{13}, \quad \cos\theta = \dfrac{\text{adj}}{\text{hyp}} = \dfrac{12}{13}, \quad \tan\theta = \dfrac{\text{opp}}{\text{adj}} = \dfrac{5}{12}$

$\csc\theta = \dfrac{\text{hyp}}{\text{opp}} = \dfrac{13}{5}, \quad \sec\theta = \dfrac{\text{hyp}}{\text{adj}} = \dfrac{13}{12}, \quad \cot\theta = \dfrac{\text{adj}}{\text{opp}} = \dfrac{12}{5}$

b. $c = \sqrt{18^2 + 12^2} = \sqrt{324 + 144} = \sqrt{468} = 6\sqrt{13}$

$\sin\theta = \dfrac{\text{opp}}{\text{hyp}} = \dfrac{18}{6\sqrt{13}} = \dfrac{3}{\sqrt{13}}, \quad \cos\theta = \dfrac{\text{adj}}{\text{hyp}} = \dfrac{12}{6\sqrt{13}} = \dfrac{2}{\sqrt{13}}, \quad \tan\theta = \dfrac{\text{opp}}{\text{adj}} = \dfrac{18}{12} = \dfrac{3}{2}$

$\csc\theta = \dfrac{\text{hyp}}{\text{opp}} = \dfrac{\sqrt{13}}{3}, \quad \sec\theta = \dfrac{\text{hyp}}{\text{adj}} = \dfrac{\sqrt{13}}{2}, \quad \cot\theta = \dfrac{\text{adj}}{\text{opp}} = \dfrac{2}{3}$

2.

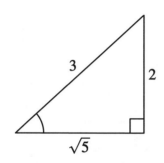

$2^2 + \left(\text{adj}\right)^2 = 3^2 \Rightarrow \text{adj} = \sqrt{5}$

$\sin\theta = \dfrac{2}{3}, \quad \cos\theta = \dfrac{\sqrt{5}}{3}, \quad \tan\theta = \dfrac{2}{\sqrt{5}}$

$\csc\theta = \dfrac{3}{2}, \quad \sec\theta = \dfrac{3}{\sqrt{5}}, \quad \cot\theta = \dfrac{\sqrt{5}}{2}$

3.

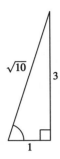

$$3^2 + 1^2 = \left(\text{hyp}\right)^2 \Rightarrow \text{hyp} = \sqrt{10}$$

$$\sin\theta = \frac{3}{\sqrt{10}}, \ \cos\theta = \frac{1}{\sqrt{10}}, \ \tan\theta = 3$$

$$\csc\theta = \frac{\sqrt{10}}{3}, \ \sec\theta = \sqrt{10}, \ \cot\theta = \frac{1}{3}$$

4. $\theta = 60° = \dfrac{\pi}{3}$ because $\cot 60° = \dfrac{\cos 60°}{\sin 60°} = \dfrac{1/2}{\sqrt{3}/2} = \dfrac{1}{\sqrt{3}} = \dfrac{\sqrt{3}}{3}.$

5. $\csc\theta = \sqrt{2} \Rightarrow \sin\theta = \dfrac{1}{\sqrt{2}} = \dfrac{\sqrt{2}}{2} \Rightarrow \theta = 45° = \dfrac{\pi}{4}$

6. **a.** $\tan 60° = \dfrac{\sin 60°}{\cos 60°} = \sqrt{3}$

    b. $\sin 30° = \cos 60° = \dfrac{1}{2}$

    c. $\cos 30° = \sin 60° = \dfrac{\sqrt{3}}{2}$

    d. $\cot 60° = \dfrac{1}{\tan 60°} = \dfrac{1}{\sqrt{3}} = \dfrac{\sqrt{3}}{3}$

7. **a.** $\sin\theta = \dfrac{1}{\csc\theta} = \dfrac{1}{3}$

    b. $\cos\theta = \dfrac{1}{\sec\theta} = \dfrac{4}{3\sqrt{2}} = \dfrac{2\sqrt{2}}{3}$

    c. $\tan\theta = \dfrac{\sin\theta}{\cos\theta} = \dfrac{1/3}{2\sqrt{2}/3} = \dfrac{1}{2\sqrt{2}} = \dfrac{\sqrt{2}}{4}$

    d. $\sec\left(90° - \theta\right) = \csc\theta = 3$

8. $(1 + \cos\theta)(1 - \cos\theta) = 1 - \cos^2\theta = \sin^2\theta$

9. **a.** $\sin 12° \approx 0.2079$

    b. $\cos 72° \approx 0.3090$

10. $\sec\theta = 2 \Rightarrow \cos\theta = \dfrac{1}{2} \Rightarrow \theta = 60° = \dfrac{\pi}{3}$

Lesson 14

1. $r = \sqrt{7^2 + 24^2} = \sqrt{49 + 576} = \sqrt{625} = 25$

$$\sin\theta = \frac{y}{r} = \frac{24}{25} \qquad \cos\theta = \frac{x}{r} = \frac{7}{25}$$

$$\tan\theta = \frac{y}{x} = \frac{24}{7} \qquad \cot\theta = \frac{x}{y} = \frac{7}{24}$$

$$\sec\theta = \frac{r}{x} = \frac{25}{7} \qquad \csc\theta = \frac{r}{y} = \frac{25}{24}$$

2. $\sin\theta = \dfrac{y}{r} = \dfrac{3}{5} \Rightarrow x^2 = 25 - 9 = 16$

The angle is in Quadrant II; hence, $x = -4$.

$$\sin\theta = \frac{y}{r} = \frac{3}{5} \qquad \cos\theta = \frac{x}{r} = -\frac{4}{5}$$

$$\tan\theta = \frac{y}{x} = -\frac{3}{4} \qquad \cot\theta = \frac{x}{y} = -\frac{4}{3}$$

$$\sec\theta = \frac{r}{x} = -\frac{5}{4} \qquad \csc\theta = \frac{r}{y} = \frac{5}{3}$$

3. $\csc\theta = 4 \Rightarrow \sin\theta = \dfrac{y}{r} = \dfrac{1}{4} \Rightarrow x^2 = 16 - 1 = 15$

$\cot\theta < 0 \Rightarrow$ the angle is in Quadrant II; hence, $x = -\sqrt{15}$.

$$\sin\theta = \frac{y}{r} = \frac{1}{4} \qquad \cos\theta = \frac{x}{r} = -\frac{\sqrt{15}}{4}$$

$$\tan\theta = \frac{y}{x} = -\frac{1}{\sqrt{15}} = -\frac{\sqrt{15}}{15} \qquad \cot\theta = \frac{x}{y} = -\sqrt{15}$$

$$\sec\theta = \frac{r}{x} = -\frac{4}{\sqrt{15}} = -\frac{4\sqrt{15}}{15} \qquad \csc\theta = \frac{r}{y} = 4$$

4. **a.** $(x, y) = (-1, 0)$, $r = 1 \Rightarrow \sec \pi = \dfrac{r}{x} = \dfrac{1}{-1} = -1$

     b. $(x, y) = (0, 1)$, $r = 1 \Rightarrow \tan \dfrac{\pi}{2} = \dfrac{y}{x} = \dfrac{1}{0}$ (undefined)

     c. $(x, y) = (-1, 0)$, $r = 1 \Rightarrow \cot \pi = \dfrac{x}{y} = \dfrac{-1}{0}$ (undefined)

     d. $(x, y) = (-1, 0)$, $r = 1 \Rightarrow \csc \pi = \dfrac{r}{y} = \dfrac{1}{0}$ (undefined)

5. $\theta' = 180° - 120° = 60°$

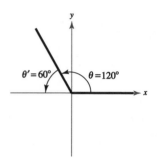

6. $\theta = 225°$ lies in Quadrant III, and the reference angle is $\theta' = 45°$.

$$\sin 225° = -\sin 45° = -\frac{\sqrt{2}}{2}, \quad \cos 225° = -\cos 45° = -\frac{\sqrt{2}}{2}, \quad \tan 225° = \tan 45° = 1$$

7. $\theta = -\dfrac{7\pi}{6}$ lies in Quadrant II, and the reference angle is $\theta' = \dfrac{\pi}{6}$.

$$\sin\left(-\frac{7\pi}{6}\right) = \sin\left(\frac{\pi}{6}\right) = \frac{1}{2}, \quad \cos\left(-\frac{7\pi}{6}\right) = -\cos\left(\frac{\pi}{6}\right) = -\frac{\sqrt{3}}{2}, \quad \tan\left(-\frac{7\pi}{6}\right) = -\tan\left(\frac{\pi}{6}\right) = -\frac{\sqrt{3}}{3}$$

8. $\sin 10° \approx 0.1736$

9. $\tan \dfrac{2\pi}{9} \approx 0.8391$

10. $I = 5e^{-2t} \sin t$

     $I(0.7) = 5e^{-1.4} \sin 0.7 \approx 0.79$ amperes

Lesson 15

1. **a.** Period: 2π ; amplitude: 3.

   Key points: $(0, 0), \left(\dfrac{\pi}{2}, 3\right), (\pi, 0), \left(\dfrac{3\pi}{2}, -3\right), (2\pi, 0)$

   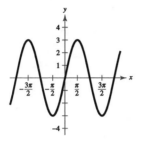

   b. Period: 2π ; amplitude: $\dfrac{1}{4}$.

   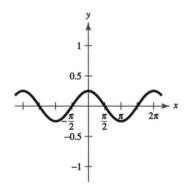

   c. Period: $\dfrac{2\pi}{1/2} = 4\pi$; amplitude: 1.

   Key points: $(0, 1), (\pi, 0),$
   $(2\pi, -1), (3\pi, 0), (4\pi, 1)$

   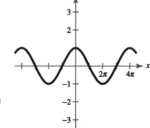

e. Period: $\dfrac{2\pi}{4} = \dfrac{\pi}{2}$; amplitude: 1.

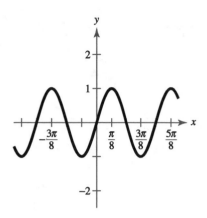

f. Period: 2π ; amplitude: 1.

Shift: Set $x - \dfrac{\pi}{4} = 0$ and $x - \dfrac{\pi}{4} = 2\pi$.

$x = \dfrac{\pi}{4}$, $x = \dfrac{9\pi}{4}$.

Horizontal shift $\dfrac{\pi}{4}$ units to the right.

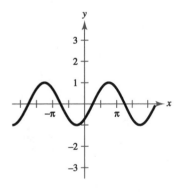

g. Period: 2π; amplitude: 1.

Shift: Set $x - \pi = 0$ and $x - \pi = 2\pi$.

$x = \pi$, $x = 3\pi$.

Horizontal shift π units to the right. In fact, $\sin(x - \pi) = -\sin x$.

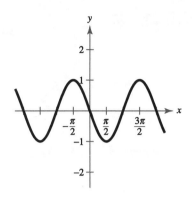

2. **a.** Period: $\dfrac{2\pi}{2\pi\big/3} = 3$; amplitude: 2.

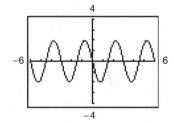

b. Period: $\dfrac{2\pi}{\pi\big/12} = 24$; amplitude: 5.

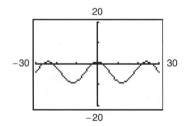

c. Period: $\dfrac{2\pi}{2} = \pi$; amplitude: 5.

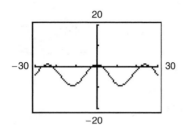

3. Period: $\dfrac{2\pi}{8\pi/3} = \dfrac{3}{4}$.

$$\frac{\text{one heartbeat}}{\left(3/4\right)} = \frac{4}{3} \text{ heartbeats/second} = 80 \text{ heartbeats/minute.}$$

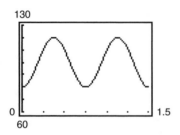

Lesson 16

1. **a.** Period: π.

Two consecutive asymptotes: $x = -\dfrac{\pi}{2}$, $x = \dfrac{\pi}{2}$.

x	$-\dfrac{\pi}{4}$	0	$\dfrac{\pi}{4}$
y	$-\dfrac{1}{2}$	0	$\dfrac{1}{2}$

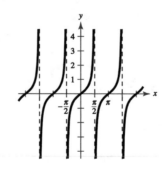

b. Period: 2π.

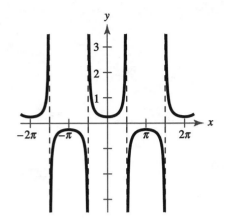

c. Period: $\dfrac{2\pi}{1\!\!\big/2} = 4\pi$.

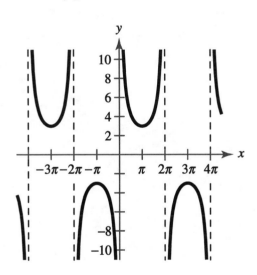

d. Period: $\dfrac{\pi}{\frac{1}{2}} = 2\pi.$

Two consecutive asymptotes: $x = 0,\ x = 2\pi.$

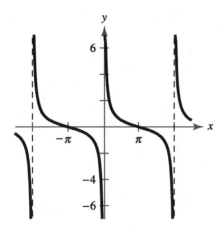

x	$\dfrac{\pi}{2}$	π	$\dfrac{3\pi}{2}$
y	$\dfrac{1}{2}$	0	$-\dfrac{1}{2}$

2. Period: $\dfrac{2\pi}{3}$. Reciprocal function: $\dfrac{2}{\sin 3x}$.

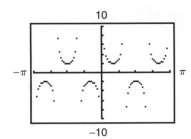

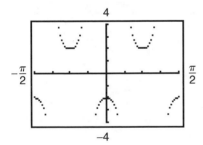

3. Period: $\dfrac{2\pi}{4} = \dfrac{\pi}{2}$. Reciprocal function: $\dfrac{-2}{\cos 4x}$.

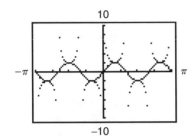

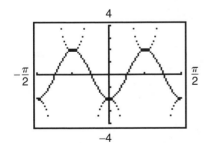

4. There are 4 solutions on the given interval: $x = -\dfrac{7\pi}{4},\ -\dfrac{3\pi}{4},\ \dfrac{\pi}{4},\ \dfrac{5\pi}{4}$.

5. The 2 graphs appear to be the same. Algebraically, $\tan^2 x + 1 = \sec^2 x \Rightarrow \tan^2 x = \sec^2 x - 1 \Rightarrow y_2 = y_1$.

6. The damping factor is e^{-x}. As $x \to \infty$, $f(x) \to 0$.

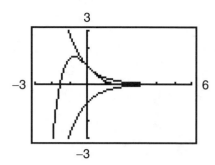

7. a.

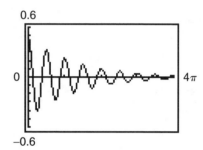

    b. The displacement function is not periodic, but damped. It approaches 0 as t increases.

Lesson 17

1. a. $y = \arccos \dfrac{1}{2} \Rightarrow \cos y = \dfrac{1}{2},\ 0 \le y \le \pi \Rightarrow y = \dfrac{\pi}{3}$

    b. $y = \arccos 0 \Rightarrow \cos y = 0,\ 0 \le y \le \pi \Rightarrow y = \dfrac{\pi}{2}$

    c. $y = \arcsin 1 \Rightarrow \sin y = 1,\ -\dfrac{\pi}{2} \le y \le \dfrac{\pi}{2} \Rightarrow y = \dfrac{\pi}{2}$

    d. $y = \arccos 1 \Rightarrow \cos y = 1,\ 0 \le y \le \pi \Rightarrow y = 0$

    e. $y = \arctan 1 \Rightarrow \tan y = 1,\ -\dfrac{\pi}{2} < y < \dfrac{\pi}{2} \Rightarrow y = \dfrac{\pi}{4}$

    f. $y = \arctan 0 \Rightarrow \tan y = 0,\ -\dfrac{\pi}{2} < y < \dfrac{\pi}{2} \Rightarrow y = 0$

    g. $y = \cos^{-1}\left(-\dfrac{\sqrt{2}}{2}\right) \Rightarrow \cos y = -\dfrac{\sqrt{2}}{2},\ 0 \le y \le \pi \Rightarrow y = \dfrac{3\pi}{4}$

    h. $y = \sin^{-1}\left(-\dfrac{\sqrt{2}}{2}\right) \Rightarrow \sin y = -\dfrac{\sqrt{2}}{2},\ -\dfrac{\pi}{2} \le y \le \dfrac{\pi}{2} \Rightarrow y = -\dfrac{\pi}{4}$

2. **a.** $\cos^{-1} 0.75 \approx 0.72$

b. $\arcsin(-0.75) \approx -0.85$

3 **a.** $\sin(\arcsin 0.7) = 0.7$

b. $\arcsin(\sin 3\pi) = \arcsin(0) = 0$

c. $\sin^{-1}\left(\tan\dfrac{5\pi}{4}\right) = \sin^{-1}(1) = \dfrac{\pi}{2}$

4. Let $y = \arcsin\dfrac{24}{25}$. Then, $\sin y = \dfrac{24}{25}$ and $\cos y = \dfrac{7}{25}$.

5. Let $y = \arctan x$. Then, $\tan y = x$ and $\cot y = \dfrac{1}{x}$.

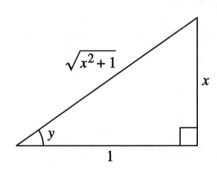

193

Lesson 18

1. Since both the sine and cosine are positive, x is in Quadrant I.

$$\tan x = \frac{\sin x}{\cos x} = \frac{1/2}{\sqrt{3}/2} = \frac{1}{\sqrt{3}} = \frac{\sqrt{3}}{3}, \ \cot x = \frac{1}{\tan x} = \sqrt{3}$$

$$\sec x = \frac{1}{\cos x} = \frac{2}{\sqrt{3}} = \frac{2\sqrt{3}}{3}, \ \csc x = \frac{1}{\sin x} = 2$$

2. $\sin(-x) = -\sin x = -\dfrac{2}{3} \Rightarrow \sin x = \dfrac{2}{3}$

Since both the sine is positive and the tangent is negative, x is in Quadrant II.

$$\cos x = -\sqrt{1-\sin^2 x} = -\sqrt{1-\frac{4}{9}} = -\sqrt{\frac{5}{9}} = -\frac{\sqrt{5}}{3}, \ \cot x = \frac{1}{\tan x} = -\frac{5}{2\sqrt{5}} = -\frac{\sqrt{5}}{2}$$

$$\sec x = \frac{1}{\cos x} = -\frac{3}{\sqrt{5}} = -\frac{3\sqrt{5}}{5}, \ \csc x = \frac{1}{\sin x} = \frac{3}{2}$$

3. **a.** $\cot x \sin x = \dfrac{\cos x}{\sin x} \sin x = \cos x$

    b. $\sec\alpha \dfrac{\sin\alpha}{\tan\alpha} = \dfrac{1}{\cos\alpha} \sin\alpha \cot\alpha = \dfrac{1}{\cos\alpha} \sin\alpha \dfrac{\cos\alpha}{\sin\alpha} = 1$

4. **a.** $\dfrac{\cos\theta}{1-\sin\theta} = \dfrac{\cos\theta}{1-\sin\theta} \dfrac{1+\sin\theta}{1+\sin\theta} = \dfrac{\cos\theta(1+\sin\theta)}{1-\sin^2\theta}$

    $$= \frac{\cos\theta(1+\sin\theta)}{\cos^2\theta} = \frac{1+\sin\theta}{\cos\theta} = \frac{1}{\cos\theta} + \frac{\sin\theta}{\cos\theta} = \sec\theta + \tan\theta$$

    b. $1 - \dfrac{\sin^2\theta}{1-\cos\theta} = \dfrac{1-\cos\theta-\sin^2\theta}{1-\cos\theta} = \dfrac{\cos^2\theta - \cos\theta}{1-\cos\theta} = \dfrac{\cos\theta(\cos\theta-1)}{1-\cos\theta} = -\cos\theta$

5. $\tan^4 x + 2\tan^2 x + 1 = \left(\tan^2\theta + 1\right)^2 = \left(\sec^2\theta\right)^2 = \sec^4\theta$

6. $\dfrac{1}{1+\cos x} + \dfrac{1}{1-\cos x} = \dfrac{1-\cos x+1+\cos x}{(1+\cos x)(1-\cos x)} = \dfrac{2}{1-\cos^2 x} = \dfrac{2}{\sin^2 x} = 2\csc^2 x$

7. **a.** $\cos^2\beta - \sin^2\beta = \left(1-\sin^2\beta\right) - \sin^2\beta = 1 - 2\sin^2\beta$

    b. $\dfrac{\tan x + \tan y}{1 - \tan x \tan y} = \dfrac{\dfrac{1}{\cot x} + \dfrac{1}{\cot y}}{1 - \dfrac{1}{\cot x}\dfrac{1}{\cot y}} \dfrac{\cot x \cot y}{\cot x \cot y} = \dfrac{\cot y + \cot x}{\cot x \cot y - 1} = \dfrac{\cot x + \cot y}{\cot x \cot y - 1}$

8. $\ln\left|\cot\theta\right| = \ln\left|\dfrac{\cos\theta}{\sin\theta}\right| = \ln\dfrac{\left|\cos\theta\right|}{\left|\sin\theta\right|} = \ln\left|\cos\theta\right| - \ln\left|\sin\theta\right|$

Lesson 19

1. $\cos x = -\dfrac{1}{2} \Rightarrow x = 120°,\ 240°$

2. $\sin x = -\dfrac{\sqrt{2}}{2} \Rightarrow 225°,\ 315°$

3. $\cot x = -1 \Rightarrow x = \dfrac{3\pi}{4},\ \dfrac{7\pi}{4}$

4. $\csc x = -2 \Rightarrow \sin x = -\dfrac{1}{2} \Rightarrow x = \dfrac{7\pi}{6},\ \dfrac{11\pi}{6}$

5. $3\csc^2 x - 4 = 0 \Rightarrow \csc^2 x = \dfrac{4}{3} \Rightarrow \csc x = \pm\dfrac{2}{\sqrt{3}}$

   $\Rightarrow \sin x = \pm\dfrac{\sqrt{3}}{2} \Rightarrow x = \dfrac{\pi}{3} + n\pi,\ x = \dfrac{2\pi}{3} + n\pi$

6. $\sec^2 x - \sec x - 2 = 0$
   $\left(\sec x - 2\right)\left(\sec x + 1\right) = 0$
   $\sec x = 2 \Rightarrow \cos x = \dfrac{1}{2} \Rightarrow x = \dfrac{\pi}{3},\ \dfrac{5\pi}{3}$
   $\sec x = -1 \Rightarrow \cos x = -1 \Rightarrow x = \pi$

7. $2\sin x + \csc x = 0$
   $2\sin x + \dfrac{1}{\sin x} = 0$
   $2\sin^2 x + 1 = 0$
   $\sin^2 x = -\dfrac{1}{2}$

   Since this equation has no real solutions, there are no solutions to the original equation.

8. When you graph $y = 2\sin^2 x + 3\sin x + 1,$ you will see that it has 3 zeros on the interval:
   $x \approx 3.665,\ 4.712,\ 5.760.$

9. When you graph $y = 3\tan^2 x + 5\tan x - 4,$ you will see that it has 2 zeros on the interval:
   $x \approx -1.154,\ 0.534.$

10. $\sin 4x = 1 \Rightarrow 4x = \dfrac{\pi}{2} + 2n\pi$

$x = \dfrac{\pi}{8} + \dfrac{\pi n}{2}$

11. a. The domain of the function is all real numbers except $x = 0$.

   b. The graph has y-axis symmetry (even function) and a horizontal asymptote at $y = 1$.

   c. As $x \to 0$, the graph oscillates infinitely often between -1 and 1.

Lesson 20

1. a. $\cos(240° - 0°) = \cos(240°) = -\dfrac{1}{2}$

   b. $\cos 240° - \cos 0° = -\dfrac{1}{2} - 1 = -\dfrac{3}{2}$

   c. $\sin\left(\dfrac{2\pi}{3} + \dfrac{5\pi}{6}\right) = \sin\left(\dfrac{9\pi}{6}\right) = \sin\dfrac{3\pi}{2} = -1$

   d. $\sin\dfrac{2\pi}{3} + \sin\dfrac{5\pi}{6} = \dfrac{\sqrt{3}}{2} + \dfrac{1}{2} = \dfrac{\sqrt{3} + 1}{2}$

2. $\sin(75°) = \sin(30° + 45°) = \sin 30° \cos 45° + \cos 30° \sin 45° = \dfrac{1}{2}\dfrac{\sqrt{2}}{2} + \dfrac{\sqrt{3}}{2}\dfrac{\sqrt{2}}{2} = \dfrac{\sqrt{2} + \sqrt{6}}{4}$

$\cos(75°) = \cos(30° + 45°) = \cos 30° \cos 45° - \sin 30° \sin 45° = \dfrac{\sqrt{3}}{2}\dfrac{\sqrt{2}}{2} - \dfrac{1}{2}\dfrac{\sqrt{2}}{2} = \dfrac{\sqrt{6} - \sqrt{2}}{4}$

$\tan(75°) = \dfrac{\sin 75°}{\cos 75°} = \dfrac{\dfrac{\sqrt{2} + \sqrt{6}}{4}}{\dfrac{\sqrt{6} - \sqrt{2}}{4}} = \dfrac{\sqrt{6} + \sqrt{2}}{\sqrt{6} - \sqrt{2}}$

This can be simplified to $\sqrt{3} + 2$. You could also obtain the same answer by using the formula for the tangent of a sum.

3. $\sin\dfrac{13\pi}{12} = \sin\left(\dfrac{3\pi}{4} + \dfrac{\pi}{3}\right) = \sin\dfrac{3\pi}{4}\cos\dfrac{\pi}{3} + \sin\dfrac{\pi}{3}\cos\dfrac{3\pi}{4} = \dfrac{\sqrt{2}}{2}\dfrac{1}{2} + \dfrac{\sqrt{3}}{2}\left(-\dfrac{\sqrt{2}}{2}\right) = \dfrac{\sqrt{2} - \sqrt{6}}{4}$

$\cos\dfrac{13\pi}{12} = \cos\left(\dfrac{3\pi}{4} + \dfrac{\pi}{3}\right) = \cos\dfrac{3\pi}{4}\cos\dfrac{\pi}{3} - \sin\dfrac{3\pi}{4}\sin\dfrac{\pi}{3} = \left(-\dfrac{\sqrt{2}}{2}\right)\dfrac{1}{2} - \dfrac{\sqrt{2}}{2}\dfrac{\sqrt{3}}{2} = -\dfrac{\sqrt{2} + \sqrt{6}}{4}$

$\tan\dfrac{13\pi}{4} = \dfrac{\sin\dfrac{13\pi}{4}}{\cos\dfrac{13\pi}{4}} = \dfrac{\dfrac{\sqrt{2} - \sqrt{6}}{4}}{-\dfrac{\sqrt{2} + \sqrt{6}}{4}} = \dfrac{\sqrt{6} - \sqrt{2}}{\sqrt{6} + \sqrt{2}}$

This can be simplified to $2 - \sqrt{3}$. You could also obtain the same answer by using the formula for the tangent of a sum.

4. $\cos 60° \cos 20° - \sin 60° \sin 20° = \cos\left(60° + 20°\right) = \cos 80°$

5. $\cos\dfrac{\pi}{9}\cos\dfrac{\pi}{7} - \sin\dfrac{\pi}{9}\sin\dfrac{\pi}{7} = \cos\left(\dfrac{\pi}{9} + \dfrac{\pi}{7}\right) = \cos\left(\dfrac{16\pi}{63}\right)$

6. First, note that both u and v are in Quadrant II so that you have $\cos u = -\sqrt{1 - \sin^2 u} = -\dfrac{12}{13}$ and

$\sin v = \sqrt{1 - \cos^2 v} = \dfrac{4}{5}$. Hence, $\tan u = -\dfrac{5}{12}$ and $\tan v = -\dfrac{4}{3}$.

$$\tan(u+v) = \frac{\tan u + \tan v}{1 - \tan u \tan v} = \frac{\left(-\frac{5}{12}\right) + \left(-\frac{4}{3}\right)}{1 - \left(-\frac{5}{12}\right)\left(-\frac{4}{3}\right)} = \frac{-\frac{63}{36}}{\frac{16}{36}} = -\frac{63}{16}$$

7. $\sin^{-1} 1 = \dfrac{\pi}{2}$ because $\sin\dfrac{\pi}{2} = 1$. $\cos^{-1} 1 = 0$ because $\cos 0 = 1$.

$$\sin\left(\sin^{-1} 1 + \cos^{-1} 1\right) = \sin\left(\dfrac{\pi}{2} + 0\right) = 1$$

8. $\sin(x+y) + \sin(x-y) = (\sin x \cos y + \sin y \cos x) + (\sin x \cos y - \sin y \cos x) = 2\sin x \cos y$

9. $8\sin x \cos x = 4(2\cos x \sin x) = 4\sin 2x$

10. $\sin^2 2x = \dfrac{1 - \cos 4x}{2} = \dfrac{1}{2}\left(1 - \cos 4x\right)$

Lesson 21

1. $\sin B = \dfrac{b\sin A}{a} = \dfrac{5\sin\left(36°\right)}{8} \approx 0.3674 \Rightarrow B \approx 21.6°$

$C = 180° - A - B = 180° - 36° - 21.6° = 122.4°$

$c = \dfrac{a}{\sin A}\left(\sin C\right) = \dfrac{8}{\sin 36°}\left(\sin 122.4°\right) \approx 11.49$

2. $\sin C = \dfrac{c\sin A}{a} = \dfrac{10\sin\left(60°\right)}{9} = \dfrac{10}{9}\dfrac{\sqrt{3}}{2} \approx 0.9623 \Rightarrow C \approx 74.2°$ or $C \approx 105.8°$

Case 1: $C \approx 74.2°$, $B = 180° - A - C = 45.8°$

$b = \dfrac{a}{\sin A}\left(\sin B\right) = \dfrac{9}{\sin 60°}\left(\sin 45.8°\right) \approx 7.45$

Case 2: $C \approx 105.8°$, $B = 180° - A - C = 14.2°$

$b = \dfrac{a}{\sin A}\left(\sin B\right) = \dfrac{9}{\sin 60°}\left(\sin 14.2°\right) \approx 2.55$

3. $B = 180° - A - C = 180° - 102.4° - 16.7° = 60.9°$

$$b = \frac{a}{\sin A}(\sin B) = \frac{21.6}{\sin 102.4°}(\sin 60.9°) \approx 19.32$$

$$c = \frac{a}{\sin A}(\sin C) = \frac{21.6}{\sin 102.4°}(\sin 16.7°) \approx 6.36$$

4. $\sin B = \dfrac{b \sin A}{a} = \dfrac{20 \sin 76°}{18} \approx 1.078.$ No solution.

5. $\sin B = \dfrac{b \sin A}{a} = \dfrac{12.8 \sin 58°}{4.5} \approx 2.26.$ No solution.

6. $A = \dfrac{1}{2}ab \sin C = \dfrac{1}{2}(6)(10)\sin(110°) \approx 28.2$ square units

7. $A = \dfrac{1}{2}bc \sin A = \dfrac{1}{2}(67)(85)\sin(38°45') \approx 1782.3$ square units

8. The triangle in the figure is isosceles, and the other 2 angles measure $70°$ each. Using the law of sines, you can find the radius and length.

Radius: $\dfrac{r}{\sin 70°} = \dfrac{3000}{\sin 40°} \Rightarrow r = \dfrac{3000 \sin 70°}{\sin 40°} \approx 4385.71$ feet

Length: $s = r\theta \approx (4385.71)40°\left(\dfrac{\pi}{180°}\right) \approx 3061.80$ feet

Lesson 22

1. $\cos A = \dfrac{b^2 + c^2 - a^2}{2bc} = \dfrac{64 + 144 - 36}{2(8)(12)} \approx 0.8958 \Rightarrow A \approx 26.4°$

$\sin B = \dfrac{b \sin A}{a} = \dfrac{8 \sin 26.4°}{6} \approx 0.5928 \Rightarrow B \approx 36.3°$

$C = 180° - 26.4° - 36.3° = 117.3°$

2. $a^2 = b^2 + c^2 - 2bc \cos A = 225 + 900 - 2(15)(30)\cos 50° \approx 546.49 \Rightarrow a \approx 23.4$

$\cos B = \dfrac{a^2 + c^2 - b^2}{2ac} = \dfrac{546.49 + 900 - 225}{2(23.4)(30)} \approx 0.8708 \Rightarrow B \approx 29.4°$

$C = 180° - 50° - 29.4° = 100.6°$

3. $\cos C = \dfrac{a^2 + b^2 - c^2}{2ab} = \dfrac{81 + 144 - 225}{2(9)(12)} = 0 \Rightarrow C = 90°\ (\text{right triangle!})$

$\sin A = \dfrac{9}{15} = \dfrac{3}{5} \Rightarrow A \approx 36.9°$

$B = 180° - 90° - 36.9° = 53.1°$

4. $s = \dfrac{a + b + c}{2} = \dfrac{5 + 8 + 10}{2} = \dfrac{23}{2} = 11.5$

$A = \sqrt{s(s-a)(s-b)(s-c)} = \sqrt{11.5(11.5-5)(11.5-8)(11.5-10)} \approx 19.81 \text{ square units}$

5. $s = \dfrac{a + b + c}{2} = \dfrac{3.5 + 10.2 + 9}{2} = \dfrac{22.7}{2} = 11.35$

$A = \sqrt{s(s-a)(s-b)(s-c)} = \sqrt{11.35(11.35-3.5)(11.35-10.2)(11.35-9)} \approx 15.52 \text{ square units}$

6. After 3 hours, the ships are located at the positions indicated in the figure.

$C = 180° - 53° - 67° = 60°$

$c^2 = a^2 + b^2 - 2ab \cos C = 36^2 + 48^2 - 2(36)(48) \cos 60° = 1872$

$c \approx 43.3 \text{ miles}$

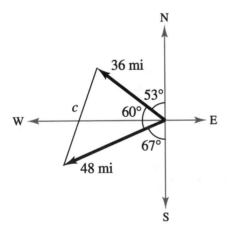

Lesson 23

1. $\mathbf{v} = \left\langle 1 - \dfrac{2}{5},\ \dfrac{2}{5} - 1 \right\rangle = \left\langle \dfrac{3}{5},\ -\dfrac{3}{5} \right\rangle$

$\|\mathbf{v}\| = \sqrt{\left(\dfrac{3}{5}\right)^2 + \left(-\dfrac{3}{5}\right)^2} = \sqrt{\dfrac{18}{25}} = \dfrac{3}{5}\sqrt{2}$

2. $\mathbf{v} = \left\langle \frac{1}{2} - \left(-\frac{2}{3}\right), \ \frac{4}{5} - (-1) \right\rangle = \left\langle \frac{7}{6}, \ \frac{9}{5} \right\rangle$

$\|\mathbf{v}\| = \sqrt{\left(\frac{7}{6}\right)^2 + \left(\frac{9}{5}\right)^2} = \frac{\sqrt{4141}}{30} \approx 2.1450$

3. $2\mathbf{u} - 3\mathbf{v} = 2\langle 4, \ 2 \rangle - 3\langle 7, \ 1 \rangle = \langle 8, \ 4 \rangle - \langle 21, \ 3 \rangle = \langle -13, \ 1 \rangle$

4. $\|\langle 6, \ 0 \rangle\| = 6$

Unit vector : $\mathbf{u} = \frac{1}{6}\langle 6, \ 0 \rangle = \langle 1, \ 0 \rangle.$

5. $\|\langle -24, \ -7 \rangle\| = \sqrt{(-24)^2 + (-7)^2} = 25$

Unit vector : $\mathbf{u} = \frac{1}{25}\langle -24, \ -7 \rangle = \left\langle -\frac{24}{25}, \ -\frac{7}{25} \right\rangle.$

6. $8\left(\frac{1}{\|\mathbf{u}\|}\mathbf{u}\right) = 8\left(\frac{1}{2}\langle -2, \ 0 \rangle\right) = \langle -8, \ 0 \rangle = -8\mathbf{i}$

7. $\mathbf{v} = \langle 4 - (-3), \ 5 - 1 \rangle = \langle 7, \ 4 \rangle = 7\mathbf{i} + 4\mathbf{j}$

8. $\|\mathbf{v}\| = \sqrt{6^2 + (-6)^2} = \sqrt{72} = 6\sqrt{2}$

$\tan\theta = -\frac{6}{6} = -1$

Since the vector lies in Quadrant IV, $\theta = 315°$.

9. $\mathbf{v} = 3\sqrt{2}\langle \cos 150°, \ \sin 150° \rangle = 3\sqrt{2}\left\langle -\frac{\sqrt{3}}{2}, \ \frac{1}{2} \right\rangle = \left\langle -\frac{3\sqrt{6}}{2}, \ \frac{3\sqrt{2}}{2} \right\rangle$

10. The direction angle is $180° + 30° = 210°$.

$\mathbf{v} = 100\langle \cos 210°, \ \sin 210° \rangle = 100\left\langle -\frac{\sqrt{3}}{2}, \ -\frac{1}{2} \right\rangle = \langle -50\sqrt{3}, \ -50 \rangle$

Lesson 24

1.

$$|6i| = 6$$

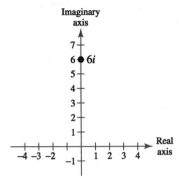

$$|-2i| = 2$$

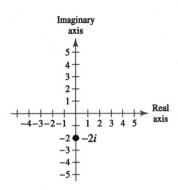

2.

$$|-4 + 4i| = \sqrt{(-4)^2 + (4)^2}$$
$$= \sqrt{32} = 4\sqrt{2}$$

$$|-5 - 12i| = \sqrt{5^2 + 12^2}$$
$$= \sqrt{169} = 13$$

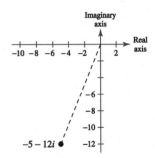

3. a. The point lies in Quadrant IV.

$$r = \sqrt{5^2 + \left(-5\right)^2} = \sqrt{50} = 5\sqrt{2}$$

$$\tan \theta = \frac{-5}{5} = -1 \Rightarrow \theta = \frac{7\pi}{4}$$

$$z = 5\sqrt{2}\left(\cos \frac{7\pi}{4} + i \sin \frac{7\pi}{4}\right)$$

b. The point lies in Quadrant I.

$$r = \sqrt{\left(\sqrt{3}\right)^2 + 1^2} = \sqrt{4} = 2$$

$$\tan\theta = \frac{1}{\sqrt{3}} = \frac{\sqrt{3}}{3} \Rightarrow \theta = \frac{\pi}{6}$$

$$z = 2\left(\cos\frac{\pi}{6} + i\sin\frac{\pi}{6}\right)$$

c. The point lies on the imaginary axis.

$$r = \sqrt{0^2 + \left(-8\right)^2} = \sqrt{64} = 8$$

$$\tan\theta = \frac{8}{0} \text{ undefined } \Rightarrow \theta = \frac{3\pi}{2}$$

$$z = 8\left(\cos\frac{3\pi}{2} + i\sin\frac{3\pi}{2}\right)$$

d. $r = 3,\ \theta = 0 \Rightarrow z = 3(\cos 0 + i\sin 0)$

4. $\left[3\left(\cos\frac{\pi}{3} + i\sin\frac{\pi}{3}\right)\right]\left[4\left(\cos\frac{\pi}{6} + i\sin\frac{\pi}{6}\right)\right] = (3)(4)\left[\cos\left(\frac{\pi}{3} + \frac{\pi}{6}\right) + i\sin\left(\frac{\pi}{3} + \frac{\pi}{6}\right)\right]$

$$= 12\left(\cos\frac{\pi}{2} + i\sin\frac{\pi}{2}\right)$$

5. $\dfrac{\cos 50° + i\sin 50°}{\cos 20° + i\sin 20°} = \cos(50° - 20°) + i\sin(50° - 20°) = \cos 30° + i\sin 30° = \dfrac{\sqrt{3}}{2} + \dfrac{1}{2}i$

6. $(2 + 2i)^6 = \left[2\sqrt{2}\left(\cos\frac{\pi}{4} + i\sin\frac{\pi}{4}\right)\right]^6 = \left(2\sqrt{2}\right)^6\left(\cos\frac{6\pi}{4} + i\sin\frac{6\pi}{4}\right)$

$$= 512\left(\cos\frac{3\pi}{2} + i\sin\frac{3\pi}{2}\right) = -512i$$

7. The cube roots of $64i = 64\left(\cos\frac{\pi}{2} + i\sin\frac{\pi}{2}\right)$ are $64^{\frac{1}{3}}\left[\cos\left(\frac{\frac{\pi}{2} + 2k\pi}{3}\right) + i\sin\left(\frac{\frac{\pi}{2} + 2k\pi}{3}\right)\right]$, $k = 0,\ 1,\ 2.$

Hence, the 3 cube roots are the following.

$$k = 0: 4\left(\cos\frac{\pi}{6} + i\sin\frac{\pi}{6}\right) = 2\sqrt{3} + 2i$$

$$k = 1: 4\left(\cos\frac{5\pi}{6} + i\sin\frac{5\pi}{6}\right) = -2\sqrt{3} + 2i$$

$$k = 2: 4\left(\cos\frac{9\pi}{6} + i\sin\frac{9\pi}{6}\right) = -4i$$

Lesson 25

    1. **a.** Solve for y in Equation 1: $y = 6 - 2x$.

            Substitute for y in Equation 2: $-x + (6 - 2x) = 0 \Rightarrow -3x = -6 \Rightarrow x = 2$.

            Back substitute: $x = 2$, $y = 6 - 2(2) = 2$.

            Answer: $(2,\ 2)$.

      b. Solve for y in Equation 1: $y = x$.

            Substitute for y in Equation 2: $5x - 3(x) = 10 \Rightarrow 2x = 10 \Rightarrow x = 5$.

            Back substitute: $x = 5$, $y = x = 5$.

            Answer: $(5,\ 5)$.

    2. **a.** We add (-1) times Equation 1 to Equation 2.

$$\begin{cases} x + 2y = 4 \\ x - 2y = 1 \end{cases} \Rightarrow \begin{cases} x + 2y = 4 \\ -4y = -3 \end{cases} \Rightarrow \begin{cases} x + 2y = 4 \\ y = \dfrac{3}{4} \end{cases}$$

$$x + 2\left(\frac{3}{4}\right) = 4 \Rightarrow x = 4 - \frac{3}{2} = \frac{5}{2}$$

            Answer: $\left(\dfrac{5}{2},\ \dfrac{3}{4}\right)$.

      b. We first interchange the equations. Then, add (-2) times Equation 1 to Equation 2.

$$\begin{cases} 2x - 5y = 0 \\ x - y = 3 \end{cases} \Rightarrow \begin{cases} x - y = 3 \\ 2x - 5y = 0 \end{cases} \Rightarrow \begin{cases} x - y = 3 \\ -3y = -6 \end{cases} \Rightarrow \begin{cases} x - y = 3 \\ y = 2 \end{cases}$$

$$x - 2 = 3 \Rightarrow x = 5$$

            Answer: $(5,\ 2)$.

      c. If you multiply Equation 1 by $\left(-\frac{1}{2}\right)$ and add to Equation 2, you obtain the inconsistent equation $0 = -4$. No solution.

      d. First, multiply both equations by 10 to eliminate the decimals. Then, multiply Equation 1 by $\left(-\frac{4}{5}\right)$ and add to Equation 2, which eliminates Equation 2.

$$\begin{cases} 2.5x - 3y = 1.5 \\ 2x - 2.4y = 1.2 \end{cases} \Rightarrow \begin{cases} 25x - 30y = 15 \\ 20x - 24y = 12 \end{cases} \Rightarrow \begin{cases} 25x - 30y = 15 \\ 0 = 0 \end{cases} \Rightarrow \begin{cases} 5x - 6y = 3 \\ 0 = 0 \end{cases}$$

            There are an infinite number of solutions: Let $y = a$, $x = \dfrac{1}{5}(3 + 6a)$.

Answer: $\left(\dfrac{1}{5}(3+6a),\ a\right)$, where a is any real number.

3. **a.** $\begin{cases} x+y+z=6 \\ 2x-y+z=3 \\ 3x-z=0 \end{cases} \Rightarrow \begin{cases} x+y+z=6 \\ -3y-z=-9 \\ -3y-4z=-18 \end{cases} \Rightarrow \begin{cases} x+y+z=6 \\ -3y-z=-9 \\ -3z=-9 \end{cases}$

$z=3,\ -3y-3=-9 \Rightarrow y=2,\ x+2+3=6 \Rightarrow x=1$

Answer: $(1,\ 2,\ 3)$.

b. $\begin{cases} 3x-2y+4z=1 \\ x+y-2z=3 \\ 2x-3y+6z=8 \end{cases} \Rightarrow \begin{cases} x+y-2z=3 \\ 3x-2y+4z=1 \\ 2x-3y+6z=8 \end{cases} \Rightarrow \begin{cases} x+y-2z=3 \\ -5y+10z=-8 \\ -5y+10z=2 \end{cases} \Rightarrow \begin{cases} x+y-2z=3 \\ -5y+10z=-8 \\ 0=10 \end{cases}$

The system is inconsistent. No solution.

4. Let $x=$ the number of touchdowns, $y=$ the number of extra points, and $z=$ the number of field goals. Then, we have the following system of 3 equations and 3 unknowns.

$$x+y+z=11$$
$$6x+y+3z=39$$
$$x-z=0$$

Solving this system, you obtain $x=4,\ y=3z=4$. (By the way, Georgia won 26-13.)

Lesson 26

1. **a.** $3A-2B=3\begin{pmatrix} 1 & -1 \\ 2 & -1 \end{pmatrix}-2\begin{pmatrix} 2 & -1 \\ -1 & 8 \end{pmatrix}=\begin{pmatrix} 3 & -3 \\ 6 & -3 \end{pmatrix}-\begin{pmatrix} 4 & -2 \\ -2 & 16 \end{pmatrix}=\begin{pmatrix} -1 & -1 \\ 8 & -19 \end{pmatrix}$

b. $3A-2B=3\begin{pmatrix} 8 & -1 \\ 2 & 3 \\ -4 & 5 \end{pmatrix}-2\begin{pmatrix} 1 & 6 \\ -1 & -5 \\ 1 & 10 \end{pmatrix}=\begin{pmatrix} 24 & -3 \\ 6 & 9 \\ -12 & 15 \end{pmatrix}-\begin{pmatrix} 2 & 12 \\ -2 & -10 \\ 2 & 20 \end{pmatrix}=\begin{pmatrix} 22 & -15 \\ 8 & 19 \\ -14 & -5 \end{pmatrix}$

2. **a.** The product is not defined because A is 3×2 and B is 3×3.

b. $AB=\begin{pmatrix} 0 & -1 & 2 \\ 6 & 0 & 3 \\ 7 & -1 & 8 \end{pmatrix}\begin{pmatrix} 2 & -1 \\ 4 & -5 \\ 1 & 6 \end{pmatrix}=\begin{pmatrix} -2 & 17 \\ 15 & 12 \\ 18 & 46 \end{pmatrix}$

3. **a.** $AB = \begin{pmatrix} 1 & 2 \\ 5 & 2 \end{pmatrix}\begin{pmatrix} 2 & -1 \\ -1 & 8 \end{pmatrix} = \begin{pmatrix} 0 & 15 \\ 8 & 11 \end{pmatrix}$

$BA = \begin{pmatrix} 2 & -1 \\ -1 & 8 \end{pmatrix}\begin{pmatrix} 1 & 2 \\ 5 & 2 \end{pmatrix} = \begin{pmatrix} -3 & 2 \\ 39 & 14 \end{pmatrix}$

b. $AB = \begin{pmatrix} 3 & -1 \\ 1 & 3 \end{pmatrix}\begin{pmatrix} 1 & -3 \\ 3 & 1 \end{pmatrix} = \begin{pmatrix} 0 & -10 \\ 10 & 0 \end{pmatrix}$

$BA = \begin{pmatrix} 1 & -3 \\ 3 & 1 \end{pmatrix}\begin{pmatrix} 3 & -1 \\ 1 & 3 \end{pmatrix} = \begin{pmatrix} 0 & -10 \\ 10 & 0 \end{pmatrix}$

4. **a.** $A = \begin{pmatrix} -2 & -3 \\ 6 & 1 \end{pmatrix}, X = \begin{pmatrix} x_1 \\ x_2 \end{pmatrix}, B = \begin{pmatrix} -4 \\ -36 \end{pmatrix} \Rightarrow AX = B$

b. $A = \begin{pmatrix} 1 & -2 & 3 \\ -1 & 3 & -1 \\ 2 & -5 & 5 \end{pmatrix}, X = \begin{pmatrix} x \\ y \\ z \end{pmatrix}, B = \begin{pmatrix} 9 \\ -6 \\ 17 \end{pmatrix} \Rightarrow AX = B$

5. There are many possible counterexamples. For example, let $A = \begin{pmatrix} 1 & 0 \\ 3 & 1 \end{pmatrix}$ and $B = \begin{pmatrix} 1 & 0 \\ 1 & 0 \end{pmatrix}$.

$A^2 = \begin{pmatrix} 1 & 0 \\ 6 & 1 \end{pmatrix}, B^2 = \begin{pmatrix} 1 & 0 \\ 1 & 0 \end{pmatrix}, A + B = \begin{pmatrix} 2 & 0 \\ 4 & 1 \end{pmatrix}, 2AB = \begin{pmatrix} 2 & 0 \\ 8 & 0 \end{pmatrix}$

$(A + B)^2 = (A + B)(A + B) = \begin{pmatrix} 4 & 0 \\ 12 & 1 \end{pmatrix}$

$A^2 + 2AB + B^2 = \begin{pmatrix} 1 & 0 \\ 6 & 1 \end{pmatrix} + \begin{pmatrix} 2 & 0 \\ 8 & 0 \end{pmatrix} + \begin{pmatrix} 1 & 0 \\ 1 & 0 \end{pmatrix} = \begin{pmatrix} 4 & 0 \\ 15 & 1 \end{pmatrix}$

6. There are many possible counterexamples. For example, let $A = \begin{pmatrix} 3 & 3 \\ 4 & 4 \end{pmatrix}$ and $B = \begin{pmatrix} 1 & -1 \\ -1 & 1 \end{pmatrix}$.

$AB = \begin{pmatrix} 3 & 3 \\ 4 & 4 \end{pmatrix}\begin{pmatrix} 1 & -1 \\ -1 & 1 \end{pmatrix} = \begin{pmatrix} 0 & 0 \\ 0 & 0 \end{pmatrix}$

$AB = 0, A \neq 0, B \neq 0$

Lesson 27

1. $AB = \begin{pmatrix} 2 & 1 \\ 5 & 3 \end{pmatrix}\begin{pmatrix} 3 & -1 \\ -5 & 2 \end{pmatrix} = \begin{pmatrix} 1 & 0 \\ 0 & 1 \end{pmatrix}$

$BA = \begin{pmatrix} 3 & -1 \\ -5 & 2 \end{pmatrix}\begin{pmatrix} 2 & 1 \\ 5 & 3 \end{pmatrix} = \begin{pmatrix} 1 & 0 \\ 0 & 1 \end{pmatrix}$

2. a. $[A \vdots I] = \begin{pmatrix} 2 & 0 & 1 & 0 \\ 0 & 3 & 0 & 1 \end{pmatrix}$ row reduces as follows:

$$[A \vdots I] = \begin{pmatrix} 2 & 0 & 1 & 0 \\ 0 & 3 & 0 & 1 \end{pmatrix} \rightarrow \begin{pmatrix} 1 & 0 & \frac{1}{2} & 0 \\ 0 & 1 & 0 & \frac{1}{3} \end{pmatrix} = [I \vdots A^{-1}] \Rightarrow A^{-1} = \begin{pmatrix} \frac{1}{2} & 0 \\ 0 & \frac{1}{3} \end{pmatrix}.$$

b. The matrix does not have an inverse because it is not square.

c. You can row reduce the augmented matrix by hand or use a graphing utility. In either case, you will obtain the following.

$$[A \vdots I] = \begin{pmatrix} 1 & 1 & 1 & 1 & 0 & 0 \\ 3 & 5 & 4 & 0 & 1 & 0 \\ 3 & 6 & 5 & 0 & 0 & 1 \end{pmatrix} \rightarrow \begin{pmatrix} 1 & 0 & 0 & 1 & 1 & -1 \\ 0 & 1 & 0 & -3 & 2 & -1 \\ 0 & 0 & 1 & 3 & -3 & 2 \end{pmatrix} = [I \vdots A^{-1}] \Rightarrow A^{-1} = \begin{pmatrix} 1 & 1 & -1 \\ -3 & 2 & -1 \\ 3 & -3 & 2 \end{pmatrix}$$

d. The inverse does not exist. If you try the matrix inverse algorithm, you will obtain a row of zeros on the left.

3. $\begin{pmatrix} 5 & 1 \\ -2 & -2 \end{pmatrix}^{-1} = \dfrac{1}{5(-2)-(-2)(1)} \begin{pmatrix} -2 & -1 \\ 2 & 5 \end{pmatrix} = \dfrac{1}{-8} \begin{pmatrix} -2 & -1 \\ 2 & 5 \end{pmatrix} = \begin{pmatrix} \frac{1}{4} & \frac{1}{8} \\ -\frac{1}{4} & -\frac{5}{8} \end{pmatrix}$

4. The inverse of the coefficient matrix $A = \begin{pmatrix} 1 & -2 \\ 2 & -3 \end{pmatrix}$ is $A^{-1} = \begin{pmatrix} -3 & 2 \\ -2 & 1 \end{pmatrix}$. Hence,

$$X = A^{-1}B = \begin{pmatrix} -3 & 2 \\ -2 & 1 \end{pmatrix} \begin{pmatrix} 5 \\ 10 \end{pmatrix} = \begin{pmatrix} 5 \\ 0 \end{pmatrix}.$$ The answer is $(5, 0)$.

5. a. $\det \begin{pmatrix} 8 & 4 \\ 2 & 3 \end{pmatrix} = 8(3) - 4(2) = 24 - 8 = 16$

b. $\det \begin{pmatrix} -7 & 6 \\ \frac{1}{2} & 3 \end{pmatrix} = (-7)(3) - 6(\frac{1}{2}) = -21 - 3 = -24$

6. Using a graphing utility or expanding along the first row, you obtain

$$\det \begin{pmatrix} -1 & 2 & -5 \\ 0 & 3 & 4 \\ 0 & 0 & 3 \end{pmatrix} = -9.$$

Note that the matrix is upper triangular, so its determinant is the product of the diagonal entries.

Lesson 28

1. **a.** $x = \dfrac{\begin{vmatrix} -1 & 11 \\ 9 & -9 \end{vmatrix}}{\begin{vmatrix} -7 & 11 \\ 3 & -9 \end{vmatrix}} = \dfrac{-90}{30} = -3 \qquad y = \dfrac{\begin{vmatrix} -7 & -1 \\ 3 & 9 \end{vmatrix}}{\begin{vmatrix} -7 & 11 \\ 3 & -9 \end{vmatrix}} = \dfrac{-60}{30} = -2$

   Answer: $(-3, -2)$.

   b. Cramer's rule cannot be used because the determinant of the coefficient matrix is 0. In fact, the system is inconsistent.

2. Let x represent the dollar sales amount. Then, you have the following.

   $0.06x = 0.03x + 350$

   $0.03x = 350$

   $\qquad x \approx \$11,666.67$

   To make the straight commission offer better, you would have to sell more than $11,666.67 per week.

3. Let x be the length and y the width. Then, you have the following.

   $$2x + 2y = 40 \Rightarrow y = 20 - x$$
   $$xy = 96 \Rightarrow x(20 - x) = 96$$
   $$20x - x^2 = 96$$
   $$x^2 - 20x + 96 = 0$$
   $$(x - 8)(x - 12) = 0$$

   Since $x \geq y$, $x = 12$ and $y = 8$ are the dimensions.

4. Let $M =$ number of oranges and $R =$ number of grapefruit.

   $$\begin{cases} M + R = 16 \\ 0.95M + 1.05R = 15.90 \end{cases}$$

   Solving this system of 2 equations and 2 unknowns, you obtain $M = 9$ and $R = 7$.

5. **a.** $\begin{pmatrix} 0 & 1 \\ 1 & 0 \end{pmatrix} \begin{pmatrix} x \\ y \end{pmatrix} = \begin{pmatrix} y \\ x \end{pmatrix}$

   This is a reflection across the line $y = x$.

b. $\begin{pmatrix} 0 & -1 \\ 1 & 0 \end{pmatrix} \begin{pmatrix} x \\ y \end{pmatrix} = \begin{pmatrix} -y \\ x \end{pmatrix}$

This is a counterclockwise rotation of 90°.

6. We substitute the 3 points into the equation of the circle to obtain the following.

$(0,\ 0): F = 0$

$(2,\ 2): 8 + 2D + 2E + F = 0 \Rightarrow D + E = -4$

$(4,\ 0): 16 + 4D + F = 0 \Rightarrow D = -4$

Hence, $E = 0$, and the equation is $x^2 + y^2 - 4x = 0$.

Lesson 29

1. $x^2 + y^2 = \left(\sqrt{18}\right)^2 \Rightarrow x^2 + y^2 = 18$

2. $\text{Radius} = \sqrt{(3-1)^2 + (7-0)^2} = \sqrt{4+49} = \sqrt{53}.$

$(x-h)^2 + (y-k)^2 = r^2 \Rightarrow (x-3)^2 + (y-7)^2 = 53$

3. We complete the square as follows.

$$\left(x^2 - 2x + 1\right) + \left(y^2 + 6y + 9\right) = -9 + 1 + 9$$
$$(x-1)^2 + (y+3)^2 = 1$$

Center: $(1,\ -3)$; radius: 1.

4. We complete the square as follows.

$$4\left(x^2 + 3x + \frac{9}{4}\right) + 4\left(y^2 - 6y + 9\right) = -41 + 9 + 36$$
$$4\left(x + \frac{3}{2}\right)^2 + 4(y-3)^2 = 4$$
$$\left(x + \frac{3}{2}\right)^2 + (y-3)^2 = 1$$

Center: $\left(-\frac{3}{2},\ 3\right)$; radius: 1.

5. Vertex: $(0, 0) \Rightarrow h = 0, k = 0$; focus: $\left(0, -\dfrac{3}{2}\right) \Rightarrow p = -\dfrac{3}{2}$.

$$(x-h)^2 = 4py$$
$$x^2 = 4\left(-\dfrac{3}{2}\right)y \Rightarrow x^2 = -6y$$

6. Vertex: $(0, 0) \Rightarrow h = 0, k = 0$; focus: $(-2, 0) \Rightarrow p = -2$.

$$(y-k)^2 = 4p(x-h)$$
$$y^2 = 4(-2)x \Rightarrow y^2 = -8x$$

7. $y^2 = -6x = 4\left(-\dfrac{3}{2}\right)x \Rightarrow p = -\dfrac{3}{2}$

Vertex: $(0, 0)$; focus: $\left(-\dfrac{3}{2}, 0\right)$; directrix: $x = \dfrac{3}{2}$.

8. The parabola opens to the right, and $p = \dfrac{1}{2}$.

$$y^2 = 4\left(\dfrac{1}{2}\right)(x+2) \Rightarrow y^2 = 2(x+2)$$

9. The parabola opens upward, and $p = 2$.
$$(x-0)^2 = 4(2)(y-4) \Rightarrow x^2 = 8(y-4)$$

10. The point $(640, 152)$ is on the parabola, so we can find the value of p.

$$x^2 = 4py$$
$$640^2 = 4p(152) \Rightarrow p = \dfrac{640^2}{608} = \dfrac{12,800}{19}$$
$$x^2 = 4\left(\dfrac{12,800}{19}\right)y \Rightarrow y = \dfrac{19}{51,200}x^2$$

Lesson 30

1. **a.** Center: $(0, 0)$; $a = 8$, $b = 3$, $c = \sqrt{64-9} = \sqrt{55}$. Vertices: $(\pm 8, 0)$; foci: $(\pm\sqrt{55}, 0)$; eccentricity:

   $$e = \frac{c}{a} = \frac{\sqrt{55}}{8}.$$

   b. Center: $(4, -1)$; $a = 5$, $b = 4$, $c = \sqrt{25-16} = \sqrt{9} = 3$. Vertices: $(4, -1\pm 5):(4, -6)$, $(4, 4)$; foci:

   $(4, -1\pm 3):(4, -4)$, $(4, 2)$; eccentricity: $e = \dfrac{c}{a} = \dfrac{3}{5}$.

   c. $x^2 + 9y^2 = 36 \Rightarrow \dfrac{x^2}{36} + \dfrac{y^2}{4} = 1$

   $a = 6$, $b = 2 \Rightarrow c = \sqrt{36-4} = \sqrt{32} = 4\sqrt{2}$

   Center: $(0, 0)$; vertices: $(\pm 6, 0)$. Foci: $(\pm 4\sqrt{2}, 0)$; eccentricity: $e = \dfrac{c}{a} = \dfrac{4\sqrt{2}}{6} = \dfrac{2\sqrt{2}}{3}$.

   d. We complete the square as follows.

   $$9(x^2 + 4x + 4) + 4(y^2 - 6y + 9) = -36 + 36 + 36$$
   $$9(x+2)^2 + 4(y-3)^2 = 36$$
   $$\frac{(x+2)^2}{4} + \frac{(y-3)^2}{9} = 1$$

   $a = 3$, $b = 2$, $c = \sqrt{9-4} = \sqrt{5}$

   Center: $(-2, 3)$; vertices: $(-2, 3\pm 3):(-2, 6)$, $(-2, 0)$. Foci: $(-2, 3\pm\sqrt{5}):(-2, 3+\sqrt{5})$, $(-2, 3-\sqrt{5})$;

   eccentricity: $e = \dfrac{c}{a} = \dfrac{\sqrt{5}}{3}$.

2. Center: $(0, 0)$; $a = 3$, $c = 2$, $b = \sqrt{9-4} = \sqrt{5}$.

   Horizontal major axis: $\dfrac{x^2}{9} + \dfrac{y^2}{5} = 1$.

3. $a = 3$, $b = 2$, $c = \sqrt{9-4} = \sqrt{5}$

   $e = \dfrac{c}{a} = \dfrac{\sqrt{5}}{3}$

4. **a.** $4x^2 - 9y^2 = 36 \Rightarrow \dfrac{x^2}{9} - \dfrac{y^2}{4} = 1$

$a = 3,\ b = 2,\ c = \sqrt{9+4} = \sqrt{13}$

Center: $(0,\ 0)$; vertices: $(\pm 3,\ 0)$; foci: $\left(\pm\sqrt{13},\ 0\right)$.

b. We complete the square as follows.

$9\left(x^2 - 4x + 4\right) - \left(y^2 + 6y + 9\right) = -18 + 36 - 9$

$9(x-2)^2 - (y+3)^2 = 9$

$\dfrac{(x-2)^2}{1} - \dfrac{(y+3)^2}{9} = 1$

$a = 1,\ b = 3,\ c = \sqrt{1+9} = \sqrt{10}$

Center: $(2,\ -3)$; vertices: $(2 \pm 1,\ -3) : (3,\ -3),\ (1,\ -3)$; foci:

$\left(2 \pm \sqrt{10},\ -3\right) : \left(2 + \sqrt{10},\ -3\right)\left(2 - \sqrt{10},\ -3\right)$.

5. $a = 2,\ c = 4 \Rightarrow b = \sqrt{16-4} = \sqrt{12}$; center: $(4,\ 0)$.

$\dfrac{(x-h)^2}{a^2} - \dfrac{(y-k)^2}{b^2} = 1 \Rightarrow \dfrac{(x-4)^2}{4} - \dfrac{y^2}{12} = 1$

Lesson 31

1. **a.** $y = -4t = -4x \Rightarrow y = -4x$

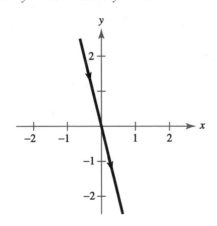

b. $x = 3t - 3 \Rightarrow t = \dfrac{x+3}{3}$

$y = 2t + 1 = 2\left(\dfrac{x+3}{3}\right) + 1 = \dfrac{2}{3}x + 3 \Rightarrow y = \dfrac{2}{3}x + 3$

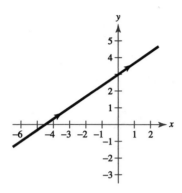

c. $x = t + 2 \Rightarrow t = x - 2$

$y = t^2 = (x-2)^2 \Rightarrow y = (x-2)^2$

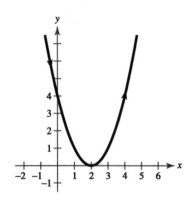

d. $\left(\dfrac{x}{2}\right)^2 = \cos^2\theta, \ \left(\dfrac{y}{3}\right)^2 = \sin^2\theta \Rightarrow \left(\dfrac{x}{2}\right)^2 + \left(\dfrac{y}{3}\right)^2 = \cos^2\theta + \sin^2\theta = 1$

$\dfrac{x^2}{4} + \dfrac{y^2}{9} = 1$ (ellipse)

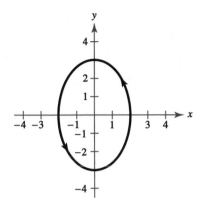

e. $x = e^{-t} \Rightarrow \dfrac{1}{x} = e^{t}$

$y = e^{3t} = \left(e^{t}\right)^3 \Rightarrow y = \left(\dfrac{1}{x}\right)^3$

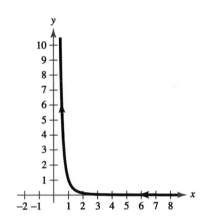

f. $x = t^3$

$y = 3\ln t = \ln t^3 = \ln x \Rightarrow y = \ln x$

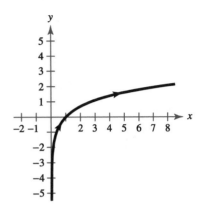

2. $\dfrac{x-h}{r} = \cos\theta, \ \dfrac{y-k}{r} = \sin\theta$

$\cos^2\theta + \sin^2\theta = \left(\dfrac{x-h}{r}\right)^2 + \left(\dfrac{y-k}{r}\right)^2 = 1$

$(x-h)^2 + (y-k)^2 = r^2$

3. $\dfrac{x-h}{a} = \cos\theta, \ \dfrac{y-k}{b} = \sin\theta$

$\cos^2\theta + \sin^2\theta = \left(\dfrac{x-h}{a}\right)^2 + \left(\dfrac{y-k}{b}\right)^2 = 1$

$\dfrac{(x-h)^2}{a^2} + \dfrac{(y-k)^2}{b^2} = 1$

4.

$$x = 2\cot\theta, \ y = 2\sin^2\theta$$

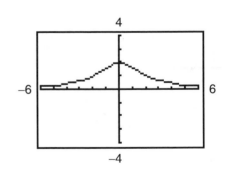

5.

$$x = \frac{3t}{1 + t^3}, \, y = \frac{3t^2}{1 + t^3}$$

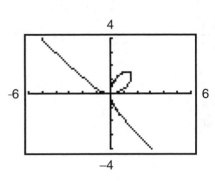

Lesson 32

1. $x = r\cos\theta = (-1)\cos\dfrac{5\pi}{4} = \dfrac{\sqrt{2}}{2}; \, y = r\sin\theta = (-1)\sin\dfrac{5\pi}{4} = \dfrac{\sqrt{2}}{2}.$

Rectangular coordinates: $\left(\dfrac{\sqrt{2}}{2}, \, \dfrac{\sqrt{2}}{2}\right).$

2. $x = r\cos\theta = \sqrt{3}\cos\dfrac{5\pi}{6} = \sqrt{3}\left(-\dfrac{\sqrt{3}}{2}\right) = -\dfrac{3}{2}; \, y = r\sin\theta = \sqrt{3}\sin\dfrac{5\pi}{6} = \sqrt{3}\left(\dfrac{1}{2}\right) = \dfrac{\sqrt{3}}{2}.$

Rectangular coordinates: $\left(-\dfrac{3}{2}, \, \dfrac{\sqrt{3}}{2}\right).$

3. $x = r\cos\theta = 4\cos\left(-\dfrac{\pi}{3}\right) = 4\left(\dfrac{1}{2}\right) = 2; \, y = r\sin\theta = 4\sin\left(-\dfrac{\pi}{3}\right) = 4\left(-\dfrac{\sqrt{3}}{2}\right) = -2\sqrt{3}.$

Rectangular coordinates: $\left(2, \, -2\sqrt{3}\right).$

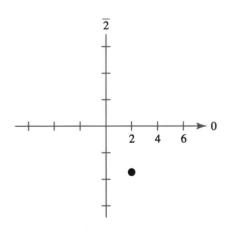

4. $x = r\cos\theta = (-1)\cos\left(-\dfrac{3\pi}{4}\right) = (-1)\left(-\dfrac{\sqrt{2}}{2}\right) = \dfrac{\sqrt{2}}{2}; \; y = r\sin\theta = (-1)\sin\left(-\dfrac{3\pi}{4}\right) = (-1)\left(-\dfrac{\sqrt{2}}{2}\right) = \dfrac{\sqrt{2}}{2}.$

Rectangular coordinates: $\left(\dfrac{\sqrt{2}}{2}, \; \dfrac{\sqrt{2}}{2}\right).$

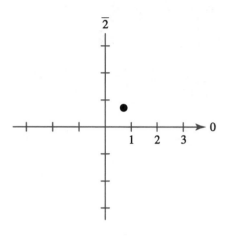

5. $r = 7; \; \tan\theta = 0 \Rightarrow \theta = \pi.$

Polar coordinates: $(r, \; \theta) = (7, \; \pi), \; (-7, \; 0).$

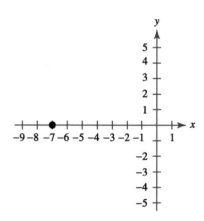

6. $r = \sqrt{3+3} = \sqrt{6}; \ \tan\theta = 1 \Rightarrow \theta = \dfrac{3\pi}{4}.$

Polar coordinates: $(r, \ \theta) = \left(\sqrt{6}, \ \dfrac{5\pi}{4} \right), \ \left(-\sqrt{6}, \ \dfrac{\pi}{4} \right).$

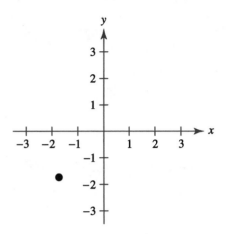

7. a. $x^2 + y^2 = 9 \Rightarrow r^2 = 9 \Rightarrow r = 3$

b. $y = 4 \Rightarrow r\sin\theta = 4 \Rightarrow r = 4\csc\theta$

c. $x = 8 \Rightarrow r\cos\theta = 8 \Rightarrow r = 8\sec\theta$

8. a. $r = 4 \Rightarrow r = 16 \Rightarrow x^2 + y^2 = 16$

b. $r = 2\cos\theta \Rightarrow r^2 = 2r\cos\theta \Rightarrow x^2 + y^2 = 2x$
$$x^2 - 2x + 1 + y^2 = 1$$
$$(x-1)^2 + y^2 = 1$$

9. If you plot some points, or use a graphing utility, you will obtain the cardioids below.

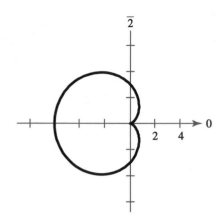

Lesson 33

1. a. $a_1 = 2(1) + 5 = 7$, $a_2 = 2(2) + 5 = 9$, $a_3 = 2(3) + 5 = 11$
$a_4 = 2(4) + 5 = 13$, $a_5 = 2(5) + 5 = 15$

b. $a_1 = \dfrac{1+1}{1} = 2$, $a_2 = \dfrac{2+1}{2} = \dfrac{3}{2}$, $a_3 = \dfrac{4}{3}$, $a_4 = \dfrac{5}{4}$, $a_5 = \dfrac{6}{5}$

2. a. $a_n = 3n - 2$ (Beginning with $n = 1$. There are many possible answers.)

b. $a_n = n^2 - 1$ (Beginning with $n = 1$. There are many possible answers.)

3. a. $\dfrac{12!}{4!\,8!} = \dfrac{12(11)(10)(9)8!}{4!8!} = \dfrac{12(11)(10)(9)}{4!} = \dfrac{11{,}880}{24} = 495$

b. $\dfrac{(2n-1)!}{(2n+1)!} = \dfrac{(2n-1)!}{(2n+1)(2n)(2n-1)!} = \dfrac{1}{(2n+1)(2n)}$

4. a. $\displaystyle\sum_{i=1}^{5}(2i+1) = (2+1) + (4+1) + (6+1) + (8+1) + (10+1) = 35$

b. $\displaystyle\sum_{i=0}^{4}i^2 = 0^2 + 1^2 + 2^2 + 3^2 + 4^2 = 30$

5. a. $\displaystyle\sum_{n=0}^{\infty}10\left(\dfrac{4}{5}\right)^n = 10\sum_{n=0}^{\infty}\left(\dfrac{4}{5}\right)^n = 10\left(\dfrac{1}{1 - \frac{4}{5}}\right) = 50$

b. $\displaystyle\sum_{n=0}^{\infty} 5\left(-\frac{1}{2}\right)^n = 5\sum_{n=0}^{\infty}\left(-\frac{1}{2}\right)^n = 5\frac{1}{1-\left(-\frac{1}{2}\right)} = \frac{10}{3}$

c. The series does not have a finite sum because $\dfrac{7}{3} > 1$.

Lesson 34

1. Odd integers are 1, 3, 5, 7, 9, 11. Hence, there are 6 ways.

2. Prime numbers are 2, 3, 5, 7, 11. Hence, there are 5 ways.

3. Total: $4(6)(5) = 120$ ways.

4. Total: $2(3)(5) = 30$ ways.

5. $\displaystyle {}_8P_3 = \frac{8!}{(8-3)!} = \frac{8!}{5!} = 8(7)(6) = 336$

6. $5! = 120$ ways

7. $\displaystyle {}_4C_1 = \frac{4!}{(4-1)!\,1!} = \frac{4!}{3!} = 4$

8. $\displaystyle {}_{14}C_{12} = \frac{14!}{(14-12)!\,12!} = \frac{14!}{2!\,12!} = \frac{14(13)}{2} = 91$ ways

9. We use a calculator to evaluate the combination.

$\displaystyle {}_{100}C_{14} = \frac{100!}{(100-14)!\,14!} \approx 4.42 \times 10^{16}$ ways

10. We use a calculator to evaluate the combination.

$\displaystyle {}_{49}C_6 = \frac{49!}{(49-6)!\,6!} = 13,983,816$ ways

Lesson 35

1. $\{(H,\,1),\ (H,\,2),\ (H,\,3),\ (H,\,4),\ (H,\,5),\ (H,\,6),\ (T,\,1),\ (T,\,2),\ (T,\,3),\ (T,\,4),\ (T,\,5),\ (T,\,6)\}$

2. $\{ABC,\ ACB,\ BAC,\ BCA,\ CAB,\ CBA\}$

3. $E = \{HTT,\ THT,\ TTH\}$

$$P(E) = \frac{n(E)}{n(S)} = \frac{3}{8}$$

4. $E = \{HHH,\ HHT,\ HTH,\ HTT,\ THH,\ THT,\ TTH\}$

$$P(E) = \frac{n(E)}{n(S)} = \frac{7}{8}$$

5. There are 12 face cards in the deck.

$$P(E) = \frac{n(E)}{n(S)} = \frac{12}{52} = \frac{3}{13}$$

6. There are 16 face cards and aces.

$$P(E) = \frac{n(E)}{n(S)} = \frac{16}{52} = \frac{4}{13}$$

7. $E = \{(1,\ 5),\ (2,\ 4),\ (3,\ 3),\ (4,\ 2),\ (5,\ 1)\}$

$$P(E) = \frac{n(E)}{n(S)} = \frac{5}{36}$$

8. The complement is $E' = \{(5,\ 6),\ (6,\ 5),\ (6,\ 6)\}$.

$$P(E) = 1 - P(E') = 1 - \frac{n(E')}{n(S)} = 1 - \frac{3}{36} = \frac{33}{36} = \frac{11}{12}$$

9. $P(E') = 1 - P(E) = 1 - 0.75 = 0.25$

10. $p + p + 2p = 4p = 1 \Rightarrow p = 0.25$

Taylor: 0.50; Moore: 0.25; Perez: 0.25.

11. The probability that all 4 units are good is $\dfrac{{}_9C_4}{{}_{12}C_4} = \dfrac{126}{495} = \dfrac{14}{55}$.

Lesson 36

1. You must find the intersection point of the 3 circles: $x^2 + y^2 = 25$, $(x+5)^2 + (y-2)^2 = 100$, and $x^2 + (y+8)^2 = 25$. Subtracting the first and third circles, you obtain

$y^2 - (y+8)^2 = 0 \Rightarrow y^2 - (y^2 + 16y + 64) = -16y - 64 = 0 \Rightarrow y = -4$. Then, from the first circle you have $x = \pm 3$. Substituting $y = -4$ into the second circle gives

$(x+5)^2 + (-6)^2 = 100 \Rightarrow (x+5)^2 = 64 \Rightarrow x+5 = \pm 8 \Rightarrow x = 3, \ -13$. Hence, $x = 3$, and your location is the point $(3, \ -4)$.

2. Let $(x, \ x^2)$ be another point on the parabola. The slope of the line joining this point and $(-3, \ 9)$ is

$$m = \frac{x^2 - 9}{x - (-3)} = \frac{(x-3)(x+3)}{x+3} = x - 3, \ x \neq -3.$$

As x approaches -3, the slope approaches $-3 - 3 = -6$. Calculus says that the slope is -6 at the point. The equation of the tangent line is $y - 9 = (-6)(x+3) \Rightarrow y = -6x - 9$.

Theorems and Formulas

Note: The number in parentheses indicates the lesson in which the theorem or formula is introduced.

angular speed (12): Central angle divided by time: $\dfrac{\theta}{t}$.

area of a triangle (21): $\text{Area} = \dfrac{1}{2}bc\sin A = \dfrac{1}{2}ac\sin B = \dfrac{1}{2}ab\sin C$.

change of base formula (9): $\log_a x = \dfrac{\log_{10} x}{\log_{10} a} = \dfrac{\ln x}{\ln a}$.

combinations (34): The number of combinations of n elements taken r at a time is $_nC_r = \dfrac{n!}{(n-r)!\,r!}$.

Cramer's rule (28): If a system of n linear equations in n variables has a coefficient matrix A with a nonzero determinant $|A|$, then the solution of the system is

$$x_1 = \frac{|A_1|}{|A|}, \ x_2 = \frac{|A_2|}{|A|}, \ \ldots, \ x_n = \frac{|A_n|}{|A|},$$

where the A_i has the same entries as A, except the ith column is the column of constants in the system of equations.

degrees to radians (12): To convert degrees to radians, multiply by $\pi/180$.

DeMoivre's theorem (24): If $z = r(\cos\theta + i\sin\theta)$ and n is a positive integer, then $z^n = r^n(\cos n\theta + i\sin n\theta)$.

determinant of the 2×2 matrix $A = \begin{pmatrix} a & b \\ c & d \end{pmatrix}$ (27): $\det(A) = |A| = ad - bc$.

exponential decay model (11): $y = ae^{bx}$, $b < 0$.

exponential growth model (11): $y = ae^{bx}$, $b > 0$.

formula for 2×2 matrices (27): If $A = \begin{bmatrix} a & b \\ c & d \end{bmatrix}$, then $A^{-1} = \dfrac{1}{ad-bc}\begin{bmatrix} d & -b \\ -c & a \end{bmatrix}$ if $ad - bc \neq 0$.

formulas for compound interest (7): After t years, the balance A in an account with principle P and annual interest rate r (in decimal form) is given by the following.

- For n compounding per year: $A = P\left(1 + \dfrac{r}{n}\right)^{nt}$.

- For continuous compounding: $A = Pe^{rt}$.

fundamental theorem of algebra (3): If f is a polynomial of degree n, $n > 0$, then f has precisely n linear factors: $f(x) = a_n(x - c_1)(x - c_2)\cdots(x - c_n)$, where c_1, c_2, ... c_n are complex numbers.

Gaussian model (11): $y = ae^{-(x-b)^2/c}$.

Heron's area formula (22): A triangle with sides a, b, and c: where $s = \dfrac{a+b+c}{2}$.

horizontal translations (15): Determined by solving the equations $bx - c = 0$ and $bx - c = 2\pi$.

intermediate value theorem (2): If a and b are real numbers, $a < b$, and if f is a polynomial function such that $f(a) \neq f(b)$, then in the interval $[a, b]$, f takes on every value between $f(a)$ and $f(b)$. In particular, if $f(a)$ and $f(b)$ have opposite signs, then f has a zero in the interval $[a, b]$.

law of cosines (22): $a^2 = b^2 + c^2 - 2bc\cos A$; $b^2 = a^2 + c^2 - 2ac\cos B$; $c^2 = a^2 + b^2 - 2ab\cos C$.

law of sines (21): $\dfrac{a}{\sin A} = \dfrac{b}{\sin B} = \dfrac{c}{\sin C}$.

linear speed (12): Arc length divided by time: $\dfrac{s}{t}$.

logistic growth model (11): $y = \dfrac{a}{1 + be^{-rx}}$.

magnitude (or length) of v (23):

matrix inverse algorithm (27): To find the inverse of the $n \times n$ square matrix A, adjoin the $n \times n$ identity matrix and row reduce. If you are able to reduce A to I, then I will simultaneously reduce to the inverse A^{-1}: $[A \ \vdots \ I] \rightarrow [I \ \vdots \ A^{-1}]$. Otherwise, the matrix A does not have an inverse.

multiplication and division of complex numbers (24): Let $z_1 = r_1(\cos\theta_1 + i\sin\theta_1)$ and $z_2 = r_2(\cos\theta_2 + i\sin\theta_2)$.

- Multiplication: $z_1 z_2 = r_1 r_2 [\cos(\theta_1 + \theta_2) + i\sin(\theta_1 + \theta_2)]$.

- Division: $\dfrac{z_1}{z_2} = \dfrac{r_1}{r_2}[\cos(\theta_1 - \theta_2) + i\sin(\theta_1 - \theta_2)]$, $z_2 \neq 0$.

Newton's law of cooling (11): The rate of change in the temperature of an object is proportional to the difference between the object's temperature and the temperature of the surrounding medium.

parametric equations (31): The parametric equations of the line through the 2 points (x_1, y_1) and (x_2, y_2) are $x = x_1 + t(x_2 - x_1)$, $y = y_1 + t(y_2 - y_1)$.

permutations (34):

The number of permutations of n elements is $n! = n(n-1)(n-2)\cdots(3)(2)(1)$.

The number of permutations of n elements taken r at a time is $_nP_r = \dfrac{n!}{(n-r)!}$.

polar coordinates conversion formula (32): The polar coordinates (r, θ) are related to the rectangular coordinates (x, y) as follows.

- $x = r\cos\theta, \; y = r\sin\theta$

-

probability (35):

- If an event E has $n(E)$ equally likely outcomes and its sample space S has $n(S)$ equally likely outcomes, then the probability of event E is given by $p(E) = \dfrac{n(E)}{n(S)}$.

- If A and B are mutually exclusive events, then $P(A\cap B) = \varnothing$, and $P(A\cup B) = P(A) + P(B)$.

- If A and B are events in the same sample space, then the probability of A or B is

- $P(A\cup B) = P(A) + P(B) - P(A\cap B).$

-

- The probability of the complement A' of an event A is $P(A') = 1 - P(A)$

product of 2 matrices (26): If A is $m \times n$ and B is $n \times p$, then their product is an $m \times p$ matrix $AB = \left[c_{ij}\right]$, where $c_{ij} = a_{i1}b_{1j} + a_{i2}b_{2j} + \cdots + a_{in}b_{nj}$.

projectile motion (31): neglecting air resistance, the path of a projectile launched at a height h feet above the ground at an angle θ with the horizontal and with the initial velocity v_0 feet per second is

Pythagorean theorem (13): In any right triangle with sides a and b and hypotenuse c, $a^2 + b^2 = c^2$.

quadratic formula (2): $x = \dfrac{-b \pm \sqrt{b^2 - 4ac}}{2a}$.

radians to degrees (12): To convert radians to degrees, multiply by $180\!\!\diagup\!\!{}_{\pi}$.

rule of 70 (8): The doubling time for a deposit earning $r\,\%$ interest compounded *continuously* is approximately $\dfrac{70}{r}$ years.

rule of 72 (9): The doubling time for a deposit earning $r\,\%$ interest compounded *annually* is $\dfrac{72}{r}$ years.

scalar multiple of a number times a matrix (26): $k\left[a_{ij}\right] = \left[ka_{ij}\right]$.

standard form of a circle (29): $(x-h)^2 + (y-k)^2 = r^2$.

standard form of ellipses (30): Standard form of ellipses with center at (h, k) and major and minor axes of lengths $2a$ and $2b$, respectively, where $0 < b < a$:

- Horizontal major axis: $\dfrac{(x-h)^2}{a^2} + \dfrac{(y-k)^2}{b^2} = 1$.

- Vertical major axis: $\dfrac{(x-h)^2}{b^2} + \dfrac{(y-k)^2}{a^2} = 1$.

- The foci lie on the major axis, c units from the center, with $c^2 = a^2 - b^2$.

standard form of hyperbolas (30): Standard form of hyperbolas with center at (h, k):

- Transverse axis is horizontal: $\dfrac{(x-h)^2}{a^2} - \dfrac{(y-k)^2}{b^2} = 1$.

- Transverse axis is vertical: $\dfrac{(y-k)^2}{a^2} - \dfrac{(x-h)^2}{b^2} = 1$.

- The vertices are a units from the center. The foci are c units from the center with $c^2 = a^2 + b^2$.

standard form of parabolas (29): Standard form of parabolas with vertex at (h, k):

- Vertical axis; directrix $y = k - p$: $(x-h)^2 = 4p(y-k)$, $p \neq 0$.

- Horizontal axis; directrix $x = h - p$: $(y-k)^2 = 4p(x-h)$, $p \neq 0$.

sum of 2 matrices of the same order (26): $\left[a_{ij} \right] + \left[b_{ij} \right] = \left[a_{ij} + b_{ij} \right]$.

sum of a finite geometric series (33): $\displaystyle\sum_{i=0}^{n} r^i = \dfrac{1 - r^{n+1}}{1 - r}$.

sum of an infinite geometric series (33): $\displaystyle\sum_{i=0}^{\infty} r^i = \dfrac{1}{1-r}$, $|r| < 1$. (If $|r| \geq 1$, the infinite series does not have a sum.)

trigonometric form of a vector (23): $\mathbf{v} = \|\mathbf{v}\|(\cos\theta\, \mathbf{i} + \sin\theta\, \mathbf{j})$. Here, the direction angle θ is the angle the vector makes with the positive x-axis.

vector operations (23): Let $\mathbf{u} = \langle u_1, u_2 \rangle$, $\mathbf{v} = \langle v_1, v_2 \rangle$, and let k be a real number.

- Addition: $\mathbf{u} + \mathbf{v} = \langle u_1 + v_1, u_2 + v_2 \rangle$.

- Scalar multiplication: $k\mathbf{u} = k\langle u_1, u_2 \rangle = \langle ku_1, ku_2 \rangle$.

Algebra Summary

Note: The number in parentheses indicates the lesson in which the concept is introduced.

Properties of Exponents (7)

Let a, b be real numbers and m, n integers.

- $a^m a^n = a^{m+n}$, $\dfrac{a^m}{a^n} = a^{m-n}$

- $a^{-n} = \dfrac{1}{a^n}$, $a^0 = 1$ $(a \neq 0)$, $\left|a^2\right| = \left|a\right|^2 = a^2$

- $(ab)^m = a^m b^m$, $\left(\dfrac{a}{b}\right)^m = \dfrac{a^m}{b^m}$

- $\left(a^m\right)^n = a^{mn}$

Properties of Logarithms (9)

- $\log_a 1 = 0$

- $\log_a a = 1$

- $\log_a a^x = x$

- $a^{\log_a x} = x$, $x > 0$

- If $\log_a x = \log_a y$, then $x = y$.

- $\log_a(uv) = \log_a u + \log_a v$

- $\log_a\left(\dfrac{u}{v}\right) = \log_a u - \log_a v$
- $\log_a u^n = n \log_a u$, $u > 0$

Graphs of Common Functions

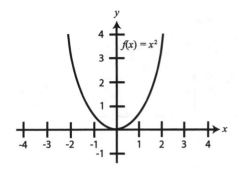

Squaring Function

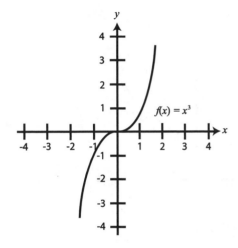

Cubing Function

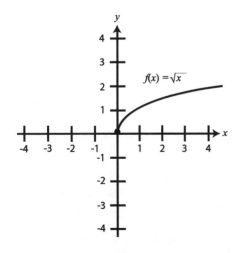

Square Root Function

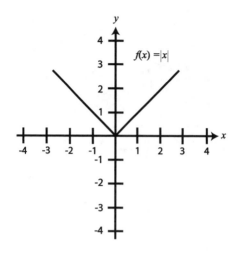

Absolute Value Function

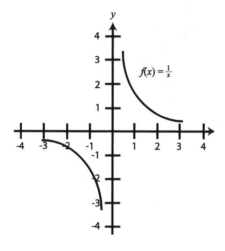

Rational Function

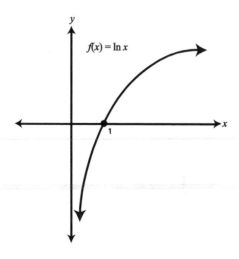

Natural Logarithmic Function

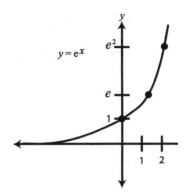

Natural Exponential Function

Exponential and Logarithmic Models

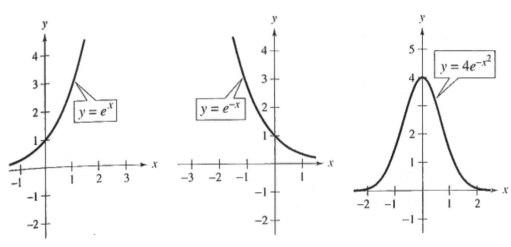

Exponential Growth Model   *Exponential Decay Model*   *Gaussian Model*

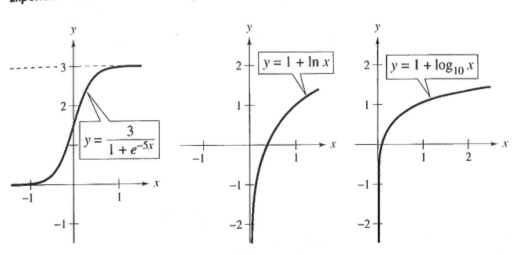

Logistic Growth Model   *Natural Logarithmic Model*   *Common Logarithmic Model*

Trigonometry Summary

Note: The number in parentheses indicates the lesson in which the concept is introduced.

Degree Measure

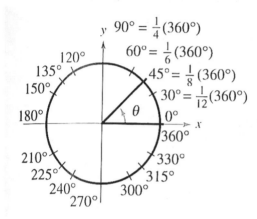

Right Triangle Trigonometry

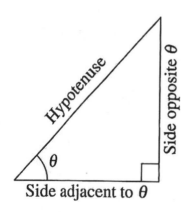

Definition of the 6 Trigonometric Functions (13)

Right triangle definitions, where $0 < \theta < \dfrac{\pi}{2}$.

$$\sin\theta = \frac{\text{opposite}}{\text{hypotenuse}} \qquad \csc\theta = \frac{\text{hypotenuse}}{\text{opposite}}$$

$$\cos\theta = \frac{\text{adjacent}}{\text{hypotenuse}} \qquad \sec\theta = \frac{\text{hypotenuse}}{\text{adjacent}}$$

$$\tan\theta = \frac{\text{opposite}}{\text{adjacent}} \qquad \cot\theta = \frac{\text{adjacent}}{\text{opposite}}$$

Circular function definitions, where θ is any angle.

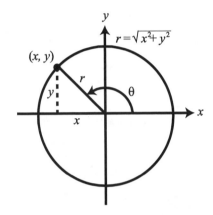

Trigonometric Functions (14)

$$\sin\theta = \frac{y}{r} \qquad \csc\theta = \frac{r}{y}$$

$$\cos\theta = \frac{x}{r} \qquad \sec\theta = \frac{r}{x}$$

$$\tan\theta = \frac{y}{x} \qquad \cot\theta = \frac{x}{y}$$

Reciprocal Identities (16)

$$\sec\theta = \frac{1}{\cos\theta}$$

$$\csc\theta = \frac{1}{\sin\theta}$$

$$\cot\theta = \frac{1}{\tan\theta}$$

Tangent and Cotangent Identities (16)

$$\tan x = \frac{\sin x}{\cos x} \qquad \cot x = \frac{\cos x}{\sin x}$$

Pythagorean Identities (13)

$$\sin^2 x + \cos^2 x = 1$$
$$1 + \tan^2 x = \sec^2 x$$
$$1 + \cot^2 x = \csc^2 x$$

Symmetry Relations (18)

$$\sin(-x) = -\sin x \qquad \cos(-x) = \cos x$$
$$\csc(-x) = -\csc x \qquad \tan(-x) = -\tan x$$
$$\sec(-x) = \sec x \qquad \cot(-x) = -\cot x$$

Sum and Difference Formulas (20)

$$\sin(u \pm v) = \sin u \cos v \pm \cos u \sin v$$
$$\cos(u \pm v) = \cos u \cos v \mp \sin u \sin v$$
$$\tan(u \pm v) = \frac{\tan u \pm \tan v}{1 \mp \tan u \tan v}$$

Cofunction Identities (18)

$$\sin\left(\frac{\pi}{2} - u\right) = \cos u$$

$$\cos\left(\frac{\pi}{2} - u\right) = \sin u$$

$$\tan\left(\frac{\pi}{2} - u\right) = \cot u$$

Double-Angle Formulas (20)

$$\sin 2u = 2\sin u \cos u$$
$$\cos 2u = \cos^2 u - \sin^2 u = 2\cos^2 u - 1 = 1 - 2\sin^2 u$$

Power-Reducing Formulas (20)

$$\sin^2 u = \frac{1 - \cos 2u}{2}$$
$$\cos^2 u = \frac{1 + \cos 2u}{2}$$

Trigonometric Values of Common Angles (14)

Trigonometric Values of Common Angles							
θ (degrees)	0°	30°	45°	60°	90°	180°	270°
θ (radians)	0	$\frac{\pi}{6}$	$\frac{\pi}{4}$	$\frac{\pi}{3}$	$\frac{\pi}{2}$	π	$\frac{3\pi}{2}$
$\sin \theta$	0	$\frac{1}{2}$	$\frac{\sqrt{2}}{2}$	$\frac{\sqrt{3}}{2}$	1	0	−1
$\cos \theta$	1	$\frac{\sqrt{3}}{2}$	$\frac{\sqrt{2}}{2}$	$\frac{1}{2}$	0	−1	0
$\tan \theta$	0	$\frac{\sqrt{3}}{3}$	1	$\sqrt{3}$	undef.	0	undef.

Inverse Trigonometric Functions (Definitions) (17)

$y = \arcsin x$ if and only if $\sin y = x$, $-1 \le x \le 1$, $-\frac{\pi}{2} \le y \le \frac{\pi}{2}$.

$y = \arccos x$ if and only if $\cos y = x$, $-1 \le x \le 1$, $0 \le y \le \pi$.

$y = \arctan x$ if and only if $\tan y = x$, $-\infty < x < \infty$, $-\frac{\pi}{2} < y < \frac{\pi}{2}$.

Graphs of Common Functions

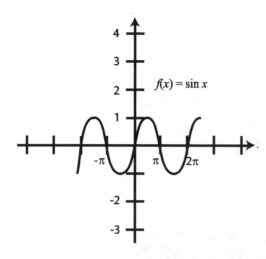

Sine Function (15)

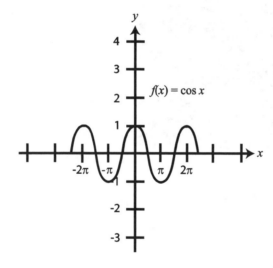

Cosine Function (15)

Tangent Function

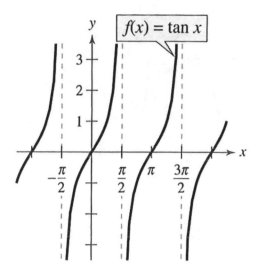

Cosecant Function

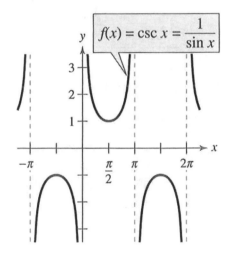

Secant Function

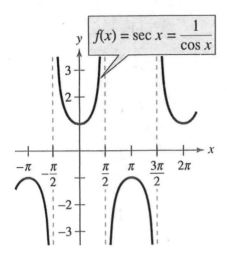

Cotangent Function

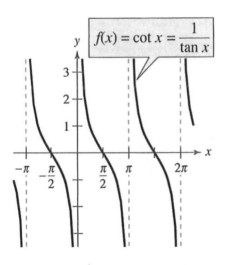

Glossary

Note: The number in parentheses indicates the lesson in which the concept or term is introduced.

absolute value function (1): $f(x) = |x| = \begin{cases} x, & x \geq 0 \\ -x, & x < 0 \end{cases}$. The absolute value of a number is always nonnegative.

absolute value of a complex number (24): *See* **complex numbers**.

acute angle (12): An angle between $0°$ and $90°$.

addition of functions (5): $(f+g)(x) = f(x) + g(x)$.

amplitude (15): Given the general sine and cosine functions $y = d + a\sin(bx - c)$, $y = d + a\cos(bx - c)$, where $b > 0$, amplitude is $|a|$. This number represents half the distance between the maximum and minimum values of the function.

angle (12): Is determined by rotating a ray (half-line) about its endpoint. The starting position of the ray is the initial side, and the end position is the terminal side. The endpoint of the ray is the vertex. If the origin is the vertex and the initial side is the positive x-axis, then the angle is in standard position.

angular speed (12): Measures how fast the angle is changing. It is the central angle divided by time: $\dfrac{\theta}{t}$.

axis of a parabola (29): *See* **parabola**.

center of a circle (29): *See* **circle**.

center of a hyperbola (30): *See* **hyperbola**.

center of an ellipse (30): *See* **ellipse**.

circle (29): The set of all points (x, y) in a plane that are equidistant from a fixed point (h, k), called the center of the circle. The distance between the center and any point (x, y) on the circle is the radius, r.

closed interval (6): Closed interval $[a, b]$ means $a \leq x \leq b$.

common logarithms (8): Logarithms to base 10.

complementary angles (12): Two positive angles are complements of each other if their sum is $90°$.

complement of an event (35): *See* **experiment**.

complex conjugate (3): The complex conjugate of $a + bi$ is $a - bi$.

complex numbers (3): The set of complex or imaginary numbers consists of all numbers of the form $a + bi$, where a and b are real numbers.

The absolute value or modulus of a complex number $a + bi$ is $|a + bi| = \sqrt{a^2 + b^2}$.

The trigonometric form of the complex number $z = a + bi$ is $z = r(\cos\theta + i\sin\theta)$, where r is the absolute value and θ is the appropriate angle given by $\tan\theta = \dfrac{b}{a}$.

n^{th} roots of a complex number: For a positive integer n, the complex number $z = r(\cos\theta + i\sin\theta)$ has exactly n distinct n^{th} roots given by $\sqrt[n]{r}\left(\cos\dfrac{\theta + 2\pi k}{n} + i\sin\dfrac{\theta + 2\pi k}{n}\right)$, $k = 0,\ 1,\ \dots,\ n-1$.

component form (23) : *See* **vector**.

components of a vector (23) : *See* **vector**.

composition (5): The composition of 2 functions is defined by $(f \circ g)(x) = f(g(x))$.

conic section (29): The intersection of a plane with a double-napped cone.

coterminal angles (12): Two angles that have the same initial and terminal sides.

degree (12): Equivalent to a rotation of $1/360$ of a complete revolution about the vertex.

degree of a polynomial function (2): *See* **polynomial function**.

dependent variable (1): $y = f(x)$ is the dependent variable, where y depends on x.

determinant (27): *See* **matrix**.

directed line segment (23): *See* **vector**.

directrix of a parabola (29): *See* **parabola**.

domain (1): The domain of a function is the set of inputs.

e (7): An irrational number, the natural base $e \approx 2.71828$ is the most important base in calculus. The corresponding function $f(x) = e^x$ is called the natural exponential function.

eccentricity of an ellipse (30): $e = \dfrac{c}{a}$.

ellipse (30): The set of all points (x, y) in a plane, the sum of whose distances from 2 distinct fixed points, called foci, is constant. The line through the foci intersects the ellipse at 2 points called **vertices**. The chord joining the vertices is the major axis, and its midpoint is the center of the ellipse. The chord perpendicular to the major axis at the center is the minor axis.

equivalent (23) : *See* **vector**.

even (2): A function is even if $f(-x) = f(x)$.

event (35): *See* **experiment**.

experiment (35): Any happening whose result is uncertain is called an experiment. The possible results of the experiment are outcomes. The set of all possible outcomes of the experiment is the sample space of the experiment, and any subcollection of a sample space is an event.

Two events A and B (from the same sample space) are mutually exclusive if A and B have no outcomes in common.

The complement of an event A is the collection of all outcomes in the sample space that are not in A, and is denoted A'.

exponential function (7): The exponential function f with base a $(a > 0, a \neq 1)$ is defined by $f(x) = a^x$, where x is any real number. The domain of the exponential function is $(-\infty, \infty)$, and the range is $(0, \infty)$. The exponential function is increasing if $a > 0$ and decreasing if $0 < a < 1$. The intercept is $(0, 1)$. The x-axis is the horizontal asymptote. The exponential function is one-to-one and hence has an inverse (the logarithmic function).

factorial notation (33): $n! = 1(2)(3)\cdots(n-1)(n)$. $0! = 1$.

Fibonacci sequence (33): $a_0 = 1$, $a_1 = 1$, $a_k = a_{k-2} + a_{k-1}$, $k > 1$.

foci of a hyperbola (30): *See* **hyperbola**.

foci of an ellipse (30): *See* **ellipse**.

focus of a parabola (29): *See* **parabola**.

full revolution (12): A full revolution around the vertex of a circle is $360°$.

function (1): A function, f, from a set A to a set B is a relation that assigns to each element x in the set A exactly one element y in the set B. The notation is $y = f(x)$, where y is the value of the function at x.

fundamental counting principle (34): Let E_1 and E_2 be 2 events. The first event, E_1, can occur in m_1 different ways. After E_1 has occurred, E_2 can occur in m_2 different ways. The fundamental counting principle says that the 2 events can occur in $m_1 m_2$ ways.

geometric series (33): *See* **infinite geometric series**.

Global Positioning System (GPS) (36): A set of 27 orbiting satellites, of which 24 are operational at any one time, and 3 are backups. At any one time, at least 4 satellites are within view of a GPS device (receiver) from anywhere in the world.

horizontal asymptote (4): The horizontal line $y = b$ is a horizontal asymptote of the graph of f if $f(x) \to b$ as $x \to \infty$ or $x \to -\infty$.

horizontal line test (5): *See* **one-to-one function**.

hyperbola (30): The set of all points (x, y) in a plane, the difference of whose distances from 2 distinct fixed points, called foci, is a positive constant. The graph of a hyperbola has 2 branches. The line through the foci intersects the hyperbola at the vertices. The line segment joining the vertices is the transverse axis. The midpoint of the transverse axis is the center.

identity matrix (26): *See* **matrix**.

imaginary numbers (3): *See* **complex numbers**.

imaginary unit *i* (3): The imaginary unit $i = \sqrt{-1}$. In other words, $i^2 = -1$.

independent variable (1): For the function $y = f(x)$, the variable x is called the independent variable.

inequalities (6): The properties of inequalities are:

$a < b$ and $b < c$ implies $a < c$ (transitivity).

$a < b$ and $c < d$ implies $a + c < b + d$.

$a < b$ implies $a + c < b + c$.

$a < b$ and $c > 0$ implies $ac < bc$.

$a < b$ and $c < 0$ implies $ac > bc$.

Let $a > 0$. Then

$|x| < a$ if and only if $-a < x < a$.

$|x| > a$ if and only if $x < -a$ or $x > a$.

infinite geometric series (33): The sum of the terms of an infinite geometric sequence is called an infinite geometric series or simply a geometric series.

infinite interval (6): Infinite interval $[a, \infty)$ means $x \geq a$. Infinite interval $(-\infty, b)$ means $x < b$.

infinite sequence (33): A function whose domain is the set of positive integers. The function values $a_1, a_2, a_3, \ldots, a_n, \ldots$ are the terms of the sequence.

initial side of a ray of an angle (12): *See* **angle**.

intersection symbol ($\cap$) (6): The expression $A \cap B$ means all numbers contained in both sets A and B.

inverse functions (5): Let f and g be 2 functions such that $f(g(x)) = x$ for all x in the domain of g, and $g(f(x)) = x$ for all x in the domain of f. Then g is the inverse of f, denoted f^{-1}. If a function has an inverse, then the inverse is unique. If f is the inverse of g, then g is the inverse of f. The domain of f is the range of g, and the domain of g is the range of f. The graphs of inverse functions are symmetric across the line $y = x$.

inverse of a square matrix (27): *See* **matrix**.

inverse trigonometric functions (definitions) (17):

$y = \arcsin x$ if and only if $\sin y = x$, $-1 \leq x \leq 1$, $-\dfrac{\pi}{2} \leq y \leq \dfrac{\pi}{2}$

$y = \arccos x$ if and only if $\cos y = x$, $-1 \leq x \leq 1$, $0 \leq y \leq \pi$

$$y = \arctan x \text{ if and only if } \tan y = x, \; -\infty < x < \infty, \; -\frac{\pi}{2} < y < \frac{\pi}{2}$$

leading coefficient (2): *See* **polynomial function**.

linear polynomial (2): Has the form $f(x) = a_1 x + a_0$ or $y = mx + b$.

linear speed (12): Measures how fast a particle moves. It is arc length divided by time: $\frac{s}{t}$.

logarithmic function (8): The logarithmic function f with base a ($a > 0$, $a \neq 1$) is defined by $y = \log_a x$ if and only if $x = a^y$. The domain of the logarithmic function is $(0, \infty)$, and the range is $(-\infty, \infty)$. The logarithmic function is increasing if $a > 0$ and decreasing if $0 < a < 1$. The intercept is $(1, 0)$. The y-axis is the vertical asymptote. The logarithmic function is one-to-one, and the inverse is the exponential function. The graphs of the logarithmic and exponential functions (with the same base) are reflections of each other across the line $y = x$.

magnitude (23): *See* **vector**.

major axis of an ellipse (30): *See* **ellipse**.

matrix (26): A rectangular array of numbers. $A = \begin{bmatrix} a_{ij} \end{bmatrix} = \begin{bmatrix} a_{11} & a_{12} & \cdots & a_{1n} \\ a_{21} & a_{22} & \cdots & a_{2n} \\ \vdots & \vdots & & \vdots \\ a_{m1} & a_{m2} & \cdots & a_{mn} \end{bmatrix}$. The order or size of a matrix is the number of rows and number of columns, $m \times n$.

Two matrices are equal if they have the same order and corresponding entries are the same.

A zero matrix is a matrix whose entries are all zero.

An identity matrix is a square matrix of all zeros except for 1's down the main diagonal.

The matrix B is the inverse of the square matrix A if $AB = BA = I$, where I is the identity matrix. A square matrix is singular if it does not have an inverse.

The determinant of the 2×2 matrix $A = \begin{pmatrix} a & b \\ c & d \end{pmatrix}$ is $\det(A) = |A| = ad - bc$.

minor axis of an ellipse (30): *See* **ellipse**.

minute (12): One minute is $\frac{1}{60}$ of a degree.

modulus of a complex number (24): *See* **complex numbers**.

multiplication of function (5): $(fg)(x) = f(x)g(x)$.

mutually exclusive events (35): *See* **experiment**.

natural base (7): The irrational number $e \approx 2.71828$.

natural logarithmic function (8): The natural logarithmic function is the inverse of the natural exponential function: $y = \log_e x$ if and only if $x = e^y$. The usual notation is $y = \ln x$.

negative angle (12): A negative angle is generated by a clockwise rotation.

n^{th} roots of a complex number (24): *See* **complex numbers**.

obtuse angle (12): An obtuse angle is between $90°$ and $180°$.

odd (2): A function is odd if $f(-x) = -f(x)$.

one-to-one function (5): A function is one-to-one if, for a and b in the domain, $f(a) = f(b)$ implies $a = b$. A function has an inverse if and only if it is one-to-one. A function is one-to-one if its graph passes the horizontal line test: Every horizontal line intersects the graph at most once.

open interval (6): Open interval $(a,\ b)$ means $a < x < b$.

orientation of the curve (31): *See* **plane curve**.

outcomes (35): *See* **experiment**.

parabola (29): The set of all points $(x,\ y)$ in a plane that are equidistant from a fixed line, called the **directrix**, and a fixed point, called the focus, not on the line. The midpoint between the focus and the directrix is the vertex, and the line through the focus and the vertex is the axis of the parabola.

parameter (31): *See* **plane curve**.

parametric equations (31): *See* **plane curve**.

period (15): Given the general sine and cosine functions $y = d + a\sin(bx - c)$, $y = d + a\cos(bx - c)$, where $b > 0$, the period is $\dfrac{2\pi}{b}$ (when angles are measured in radians). In general, a function f is periodic if there exists a positive number p such that $f(x + p) = f(x)$.

permutation (34): A permutation of n elements is an ordering of the elements such that one element is first, one is second, one is third, and so on.

phase shift (15): Given the general sine and cosine functions $y = d + a\sin(bx - c)$, $y = d + a\cos(bx - c)$, where b > 0, the phase shift is $\dfrac{c}{b}$.

plane curve (31): If f and g are functions of the variable t on an interval I, then the set of ordered pairs $(x,\ y) = (f(t),\ g(t))$ is a plane curve C. The equations given by $x = f(t)$ and $y = g(t)$ are parametric equations for the curve, and t is the parameter. As the parameter t increases, the curve is traced out in a specific direction called the orientation of the curve.

polar coordinates (32): Let $P = (x,\ y)$ be a point in the plane. Let r be the distance from the origin O to P. Let θ be the angle from the positive x-axis to the segment OP. Then $(r,\ \theta)$ are the polar coordinates of the point $(x,\ y)$.

polynomial function (2): Let n be a nonnegative integer and let a_n, a_{n-1}, $\cdots$, a_2, a_1, a_0 be real numbers with $a_n \neq 0$. The function given by $f(x) = a_n x^n + a_{n-1}x^{n-1} + \cdots + a_2 x^2 + a_1 x + a_0$ is called a polynomial function in x of degree n, where a_n is the leading coefficient.

positive angle (12): A positive angle is generated by a counterclockwise rotation.

probability (35): If an event E has $n(E)$ equally likely outcomes and its sample space S has $n(S)$ equally likely outcomes, then the probability of event E is given by $p(E) = \dfrac{n(E)}{n(S)}$.

Pythagorean theorem (13): In any right triangle with sides a and b and hypotenuse c, then $a^2 + b^2 = c^2$.

quadratic polynomial (2): Parabola with has the form $f(x) = ax^2 + bx + c$, $a \neq 0$.

radian (12): Given a circle of radius 1, a radian is the measure of the central angle θ that intercepts (subtends) an arc s equal in length to the radius 1 of the circle. $180° = \pi$ radians, and 1 radian ≈ 57 degrees.

radius of a circle (29): *See* **circle**.

range (1): The set of all outputs, which is a subset of B.

rational function (4): Can be written in the form $f(x) = \dfrac{N(x)}{D(x)}$, where $N(x)$ and $D(x)$ are polynomials. The domain of a rational function consists of all values of x such that the denominator is not zero.

recurring number (6): The horizontal line over an answer indicates a recurring number: $0.\overline{9} = 0.9999999\ldots$.

reference angle (14): Let θ be an angle in standard position. Its reference angle is the acute angle θ', formed by the terminal side of θ and the horizontal axis.

right angle (12): An angle that is $90°$.

root (2): *See* **zero**.

rule of 70 (8): The doubling time for a deposit earning $r\%$ interest compounded *continuously* is approximately $\dfrac{70}{r}$ years.

rule of 72 (9): The doubling time for a deposit earning $r\%$ interest compounded *annually* is $\dfrac{72}{r}$ years.

sample space (35): *See* **experiment**.

scalar (23): Another word for a real number.

second (12): One second is $\frac{1}{3600}$ of a degree.

standard form of a complex number (3): In $a + bi$, when $b = 0$, then the number is real.

standard position of an angle (12): *See* **angle**.

standard position of a vector (23): *See* **vector**.

straight angle (12): A straight angle is $180°$.

sum of a sequence (33): The sum of the first n terms of a sequence is represented by $\sum\limits_{i=1}^{n} a_i = a_1 + a_2 + \cdots a_n$. The index of summation is i, n is the upper limit of summation, and 1 is the lower limit.

supplementary angles (12): Two positive angles are supplements of each other if their sum is 180°.

terminal side of a ray of an angle (12): *See* **angle**.

transverse axis of a hyperbola (30): *See* **hyperbola**.

trigonometric form (3): *See* **complex numbers**.

union symbol ($\cup$) (6): The set theory expression $A \cup B$ means the set of all numbers in set A together with all the numbers in set B.

unit vector (23): The standard unit vectors are $\mathbf{i} = \langle 1, 0 \rangle$ and $\mathbf{j} = \langle 0, 1 \rangle$.

vector (23): Directed line segments having the same length and direction are called equivalent. The set of all directed line segments that are equivalent to a given $\overrightarrow{PQ}$ is a vector $\mathbf{v}$ in the plane $\mathbf{v} = \overrightarrow{PQ}$.

Given a directed line segment $\overrightarrow{PQ}$, P is the initial point, and Q is the terminal point.

The length or magnitude of a directed line segment is denoted $\left\| \overrightarrow{PQ} \right\|$.

If the initial point of a directed line segment is at the origin, then the vector is in standard position. It is uniquely represented by the coordinates (v_1, v_2) of its terminal point: $\mathbf{v} = \langle v_1, v_2 \rangle$. These coordinates are the components of the vector.

The component form of a vector with initial point $P = (p_1, p_2)$ and terminal point $Q = (q_1, q_2)$ is $\overrightarrow{PQ} = \langle q_1 - p_1, q_2 - p_2 \rangle = \langle v_1, v_2 \rangle = \mathbf{v}$.

vertex of an angle (12): *See* **angle**.

vertex of a parabola (29): *See* **parabola**.

vertical asymptote (4): The vertical line $x = a$ is a vertical asymptote of the graph of f if $f(x) \to \infty$ or $f(x) \to -\infty$ as $x \to a$, either from the right or from the left.

vertical line test (1): If a vertical line intersects a graph in more than one point, then the graph is not the graph of a function.

vertical translation (15): Given the general sine and cosine functions $y = d + a\sin(bx - c)$, $y = d + a\cos(bx - c)$, where $b > 0$, the constant d determines the vertical translation.

vertices of a hyperbola (30): *See* **hyperbola**.

vertices of an ellipse (30): *See* **ellipse**.

zero (2): A root of a function $y = f(x)$ is a number a such that $f(a) = 0$.

zero matrix (26): *See* **matrix**.

Bibliography

Boswell, Laurie, Timothy D. Kanold, Ron Larson, and Lee Stiff. *McDougal Littell Algebra 2*. 5th ed. Boston, MA: Houghton Mifflin, 2003. This is a comprehensive intermediate algebra text with excellent coverage of many different topics, including a good section on matrix algebra. Real-world applications are plentiful and each chapter has many problems with solutions at the back of the book.

Edwards, Bruce, Robert Hostetler, and Ron Larson. *Precalculus: A Graphing Approach*. 5th ed. Boston, MA: Houghton Mifflin, 2008. This textbook provides a thorough coverage of precalculus. The book encourages the use of graphing technology. These Great Courses lectures are based on this best-selling textbook.

Edwards, Bruce, and Ron Larson. *Calculus*. 9th ed. Florence, KY: Brooks/Cole, 2010. A leading calculus textbook at both universities and high schools. Many of the calculus applications covered in this course are developed in this best-selling textbook.

Saxon, John. *Algebra 2*. Norman, OK: Saxon Publishers, Inc., 1997. A strong supportive text for the course. Real-world problems are included along with applications to other subjects such as physics and chemistry.

Algebra I Texts for Review:

Saxon, John. *Algebra I: An Incremental Development*. Norman, OK: Saxon Publishers, Inc., 1997. A strong review text.

Selby, Peter, and Steve Slavin. *Practical Algebra: A Self-Teaching Guide*. 2nd ed. Hoboken, NJ: John Wiley and Sons, 1991. This book provides all the basic concepts and tools of algebra with practical, real-life examples and applications and thousands of practice problems, questions, and answers.

Notes

Notes

Notes

Notes

Notes